THE TIMES
TOURNAMENT OF THE MIND

Harold Gale, Nathan Tromans and Carole Clarke

D1312839

TIMES BOOKS

Published by
Times Books Limited,
16 Golden Square,
London W1R 4BN
Copyright © Times Books Limited 1988

British Library Cataloguing in Publication Data
The Times tournament of the mind.
  1. Puzzles – Collections
  I. Gale, Harold   II. Tromans, Nathan
  III. Clarke, Carole
  793.73

  ISBN 0-7230-0312-2

Photoset by
Rowland Phototypesetting Limited,
Bury St Edmunds, Suffolk

Printed and bound in
Great Britain by
Scotprint Limited, Musselburgh

FOREWORD

The Times Tournament of the Mind must have been one of the greatest success stories in newspaper competition history. Despite the fact that entrants had to assiduously follow the competition for a full 20 days, collecting entry coupons as they went, the total participation was 31,272 readers. The level of entry was astounding, the achievement factor remarkable. Over 70% of competitors had 90% of all the puzzles correct.

This book follows the competition format as closely as possible. It contains 50 rounds of new puzzles, and, as the rounds progress, the degree of difficulty increases.

All the puzzles can be solved by accepting the instructions as they are given. You do not need a degree in astrophysics to solve the planets puzzle, nor one in the use of English to understand the meanings of words. Common sense and everyday usage are the keys. The Trivia sections have been taken from one reference book only – *The Macmillan Encyclopaedia*. Too often a variety of references disagree. I hope that you will enjoy puzzling your way through to the 50th round. It is a good training manual for next year's contest in *The Times*.

Neither this book nor the competition itself would have been possible had not my two close colleagues, Carole Clarke and Nathan Tromans, been so willing to devote virtually every waking hour to assist in their preparation. I owe them my undying thanks. I should also like to thank the following members of staff at *The Times*: Charles Wilson, the Editor, Michael Hoy, John Stockley, and Graham King to whom I owe the original idea).

Anyone interested in joining Mensa should write for a test to Mensa, Freepost, Wolverhampton WV2 1BR.

Harold Gale
Executive Director of British Mensa.
May 1988.

LOGIC Each row, column and diagonal line containing five numbers adds up to 100. You must fill in the missing numbers to discover the value of the question mark. These are the numbers which have been missed out but they are jumbled up.

25 25 15 15 14 16 20 24 26

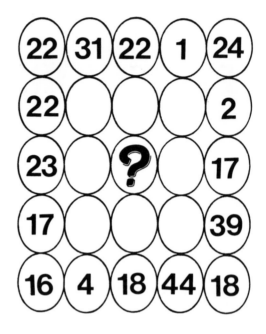

22	31	22	1	24
22				2
23		?		17
17				39
16	4	18	44	18

DIAGRAMMATIC Look at the diagram and by working out the logic fill in the missing distance.

Canada 42

44 Poland Mongolia 56

? Peru

ERBAL Which word of five letters can be
aced after HIGH, DAY and STAR in order to
rm three new words?

MATHS If you look at the following groups
of figures you should be able to work out the
logic which will enable you to discover the
value of the question mark.

(16 3 4 = 52)   (20 4 5 = 85)

(21 2 9 = 51)   (23 6 8 = ?)

ISCELLANEOUS You look at the change
your piggy bank. It totals £58.29 and is
ade up of an equal number of five coins of
e realm. You have 67 coins of each value.
an you tell us what the coins are?

TRIVIA

1 Which nocturnal African mammal is also
known as the ant bear?

2 Who became president of America in 1923?

3 What do the initials ILO stand for in relation
to the United Nations?

4 Which is the smallest county in Eire?

5 Which British actor played Archie Rice in
The Entertainer (1957)?

WORKINGS

NOTE: All the answers are to be found at the
back of the book.

ANSWERS

LOGIC   Look at this diagram of three scales. Can you work out the logic and tell us how many spades are needed in place of the question mark to make the scales balance?

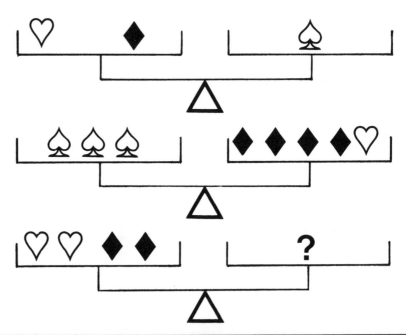

DIAGRAMMATIC   Start at the bottom left-hand corner of the diagram and follow the arrows to the top right-hand corner. Add the values shown in the white circle but take off three for every black circle encountered. How many different scores can you get and what are they?

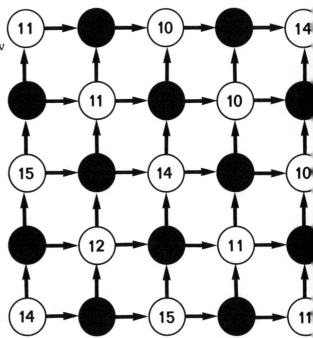

VERBAL Which four-letter word can you place between the two following words to create two new words?

FARM (. . . .) ATE

MATHS Can you replace the question marks with three mathematical symbols so that the equation is completed:

(15 ? 3) ? 4 ? 16 = 27¼

MISCELLANEOUS At the exclusive hunt ball the total takings amounted to £3240. More than 82 people attended but less than 100. Each person paid the same for a ticket in full pounds, no pence. How many people attended and how much did each pay?

TRIVIA

1 Which is the most northerly province of South Africa?

2 Which composer wrote *Fantasia on a Theme by Tallis*?

3 Who was in charge of RAF Fighter Command in October 1940?

4 What is the common name for *Convallaria Majalis*?

5 What is ALGOL?

WORKINGS

ANSWERS

LOGIC In this diagram the letters of the word PUMA can be traced in any order several times. You must always start at the centre 'P' and move from square to touching square in any direction except diagonally. Once you have found one set of letters you count that as one and start again. How many different routes can you find?

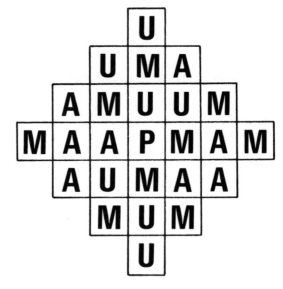

DIAGRAMMATIC Look at the diagram and work out how many different ways there are of scoring 22. You start at any corner and move inwards along the lines shown adding the value of the corner to any four values you pass through. You can only use one corner with each attempt.

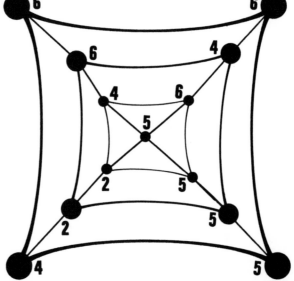

VERBAL By using every letter of this sentence once only you can find three words closely associated with building. Can you tell what they are? Here is the sentence:

ACROSS NICK'S TABLE

MATHS There is a relationship between all the numbers of each triangle. Discover what this is and you should be able to work out the logic which will enable you to discover the value of the question mark.

4	2	1	6
24	12	14	?
3 2 6	1 7	2 3	2

MISCELLANEOUS A plane maintains an average speed of 696 mph from airport A to airport B. It then returns from B to A over exactly the same distance at an average speed of 145 mph. What was the average speed for the whole journey?

TRIVIA

1 Where would you find Mount Aso?

2 Who wrote *Agnes Gray*?

3 Who is the patron saint of France?

4 What is a Gar?

5 Which hard, brittle metal was discovered in 1803 by C. Tennant?

WORKINGS

ANSWERS

LOGIC   How many squares of any size can you count in this diagram?

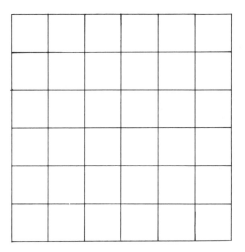

DIAGRAMMATIC   Look at the diagram and tell us how many times you can form the word EWE. Treat every E as a different letter and also every W.

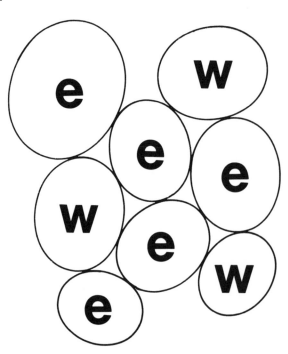

Can you replace the first letter of each of the words either side of the brackets with another letter so that a new word is formed? When you read the letters together they will form an animal.

TALK ( ) BALL

MADE ( ) WAVE

BARN ( ) WAGER

SAVES ( ) WITHER

WART ( ) COUGH

SCORN ( ) ODD

RAFT ( ) BARE

MATHS Can you work out what should be the next number in the following series of numbers?

15 21 15 12 14 10 9 7 5 ?

ISCELLANEOUS In the jungle there are some rather peculiar insects. Some have 4 wings, some have 8 wings, some have 12 wings and some have 16 wings. You have just counted 920 wings which came from an equal number of insects of each kind. How many insects of each type have you discovered?

TRIVIA

1 Which Chancellor of Germany was involved in the Kulturkampf?

2 In which country would you find the Nore?

3 Which town, the site of a major NATO base, experienced a huge fire in April 1988?

4 Which biblical character was reputed to have brought the Holy Grail to England?

5 What is a newton?

WORKINGS

ANSWERS

LOGIC Look at this series and tell us which letter you think should come next?

A S D F G H ?

DIAGRAMMATIC This puzzle is based on snakes and ladders. You have to get from start to finish. The letters and numbers in each square are highly significant. You start on the bottom line on any of the five squares and have to tell us how many squares away from start this will be. If you land on the bottom of an arrow you follow it to its head.

F	*2r*	*4d*	*1d*	*1r*	*2d*
2d	*2r*	*1l*	*3d*	*4d*	*5l*
2u	*1u*			*1u*	*3l*
2r	*2u*	*2d*	*2r*	*2u*	
	3r	*2l*	*1d*	*4u*	*4l*
1r	*5u*	*3r*	*3u*	*4l*	*1u*
S	*3u*	*5u*	*3u*	*4u*	*1l*

VERBAL   I am a five-lettered figure. Change a letter and you could be in trouble. Change a letter of the second word and this time you will find I am useful to see by. Finally change a letter of the third word and I become an essential sense. What is the last word?

MATHS   If you look at the diagram you will see that two planets are peacefully in orbit around a star. Both move clockwise. The outer planet takes 60 years to complete an orbit whilst the inner one takes 24 years. At the moment the planets are in line with each other and their sun. Can you tell us when they will next form a line with each other and their sun?

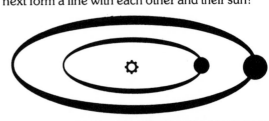

MISCELLANEOUS   Your clock is correct at midnight but loses 13 minutes per hour. You look at the clock and see that it shows 11.45 pm. You know that the clock had stopped exactly 2 hours ago. What is the correct time now?

TRIVIA

1 On which side in the English Civil War did the New Model Army fight?

2 Who wrote *Hernani*?

3 What kind of bird is a condor?

4 Who invented the Spinning Jenny?

5 How many cross members has a Papal cross?

WORKINGS

ANSWERS

LOGIC In this diagram the squares represent sections in a supermarket. Each section is 10½ feet long. Baby A passes 7 sections to get to its pram, baby B 9, baby C 12 and baby D 8. If baby A travels at 26 feet per minute, baby B at 25 feet per minute, baby C 31 feet per minute and baby D at 18 feet per minute, which will arrive at the pram first, assuming that they all start at the same time?

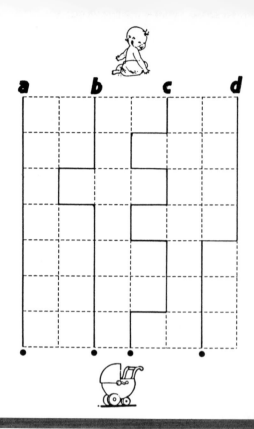

DIAGRAMMATIC Can you find the square which contains the first arrow of the string of arrows which passes through the most squares?

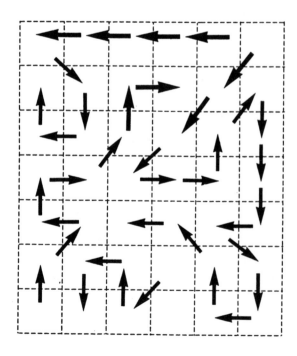

VERBAL Which five-lettered word can be placed before the following words to create four new words? Here are the words:

RODE   ION   OR   RET

MATHS A tramp collects cigar ends from which he makes full cigars. He has amassed 786 ends. He knows that he can make one full cigar from 11 ends. How many full cigars can he make and smoke altogether?

MISCELLANEOUS Four cog wheels are in constant mesh. The largest cog has 165 teeth, the next 45 teeth, the next 40 teeth and the smallest has 32 teeth. If they start revolving now, how many revolutions will the largest cog have made before all the cogs are back in the same position?

TRIVIA

1 Which Greek mythological person repopulated the Earth with his wife, Pyrrha, after the flood sent by Zeus?

2 Between 1923 and 1930 a golfer won four US and three British Open championships. Who was he?

3 Who created a scale of hardness of metals around the turn of the 18th century?

4 What is a Natterjack?

5 Which river flows through Texas and joins the Rio Grande?

WORKINGS

ANSWERS

LOGIC   The diagram is of an unfolded cube. Which of the six cubes below it is not a made-up version of the flattened one?

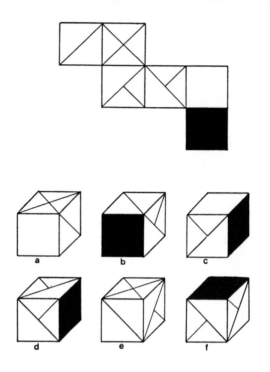

a

b

c

d

e

f

DIAGRAMMATIC   You must find the segment in this diagram which will start you off. You will then stop on every segment once only until you finish in the last segment. Here are some clues: C means clockwise, A means anti-clockwise, I means in and O means out. The numbers signify the number of moves. Which segment should you start in?

1i

5a

6c

7c

1o

1o

F

1o

4c

5c

6c

5a

6c

3a

3a

1i

2i

VERBAL The groups of letters which follow are jumbled words. You must unscramble the words and discover the most obvious odd one out.

BRASE PRASE CLEAN PROTO

MATHS In a game of 12 players which lasts for exactly 60 minutes, there are three reserves who alternate equally with each player in the team. This means that all the players, including reserves are on the pitch for the same amount of time. How many minutes for each player is this?

MISCELLANEOUS In a 150-metre race John beat Peter by 15 metres. They decide to run the race again but this time Peter starts on the 150-metre start-line whilst John starts exactly 16½ metres behind it. They both complete the race at exactly the same running speed as before. Unlikely, we know, but in puzzles anything can happen. Can you tell us who won the second race?

TRIVIA

1 Which chemical element has the symbol Sb?

2 Which Chinese goddess lives on the moon in the form of a toad?

3 What is the name of the military base in North Kentucky which was established in 1917?

4 What is the largest of the bivalve molluscs?

5 What fish is also called the White Whale?

WORKINGS

ANSWERS

LOGIC   Here is a map of a one-way street system. Can you tell us how many legal ways there are of getting from A to B?

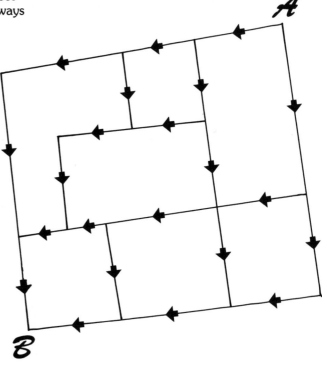

DIAGRAMMATIC   In the diagram the planet orbits the sun once every 10¼ years. The asteroid has entered an orbit which intersects that of the planet and takes 24 years to complete. If the asteroid is 45 degrees away from the intersection point when, if ever, will it collide with the planet?

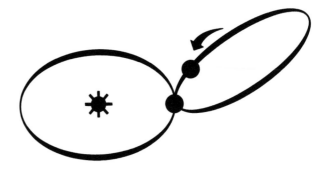

VERBAL Can you think of two words of the same six letters which will replace the blanks in this sentence:

The BLANK was furious to find the school report floating in the BLANK

MATHS A car travels at a speed of 80 miles per hour. Its fuel consumption is 25 miles to the gallon. It has a 10-gallon tank which was full when it started but at that very moment began to leak fuel. After 100 miles the car stops with a completely empty tank. How many gallons per hour was it losing?

MISCELLANEOUS Can you read the following message written in code? To help you we have placed the vowels in their correct place below the coded message. Here is the message:

M XLMRO XLIVIJSVI M EQ

I ★★ I ★★ ★★E★E★O★E I A★

TRIVIA

1 Who in Greek legend was the daughter of Zeus and Leda and was famed for her supreme beauty?

2 In which dialect of the Lowlands of Scotland did Robert Burns write?

3 Which jazz clarinettist and soprano saxophone player achieved wide recognition after a tour of Europe and subsequently worked with Duke Ellington?

4 Which Scottish poet was nicknamed 'the Ettrick Shepherd'?

5 Which city is every Muslim expected to visit at least once?

WORKINGS

ANSWERS

LOGIC In this grid you will notice that the letters are three of the ones used to spell JUDGE. You have to fill the other squares with the five letters of the word JUDGE in such a way that no two squares in the same horizontal, vertical or diagonal line are to contain the same letter. A diagonal line can contain any number of squares. Which letter should replace the question mark?

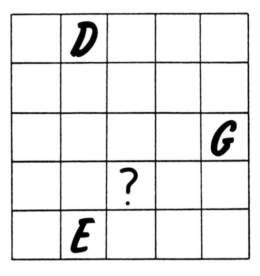

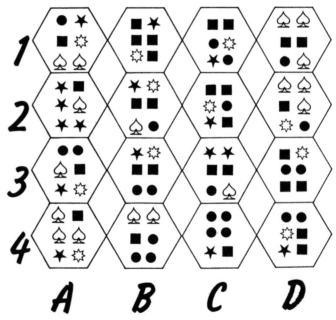

DIAGRAMMATIC Which of the squares in this diagram contain the same symbols which need not be in the same order?

VERBAL MANY can become LESS by changing one letter at a time. Each alteration, however, must give a new acceptable word. What is the least number of changes you must make and what are they?

MATHS In a football pools syndicate the winnings amounted to £1475. There were more than 30 people in the syndicate but less than 100. Each won exactly the same number of pounds, no pence were involved. Can you tell us the number of people and the amount each person won?

MISCELLANEOUS Your bath is pretty conventional. It has two taps and a drainage hole. One of the taps will completely fill the bath in 23 minutes if the plug is in the hole, whilst the other would take 14 minutes to perform the same function. With a filled bath and the taps off the time needed to drain it would be 28 minutes. Assuming that you have left both taps on and the plug out, how long will it take for the bath to be completely filled?

TRIVIA

1 What is Black Rod?

2 Which British comedian appeared in the film *Those Magnificent Men in their Flying Machines* and died three years later in 1968.

3 What word is given to the study of earthquakes?

4 Which city in the USA was notorious for its gangster activities, especially those of Al Capone?

5 What kind of asp probably killed Cleopatra?

WORKINGS

ANSWERS

LOGIC The letters of the word AMSTERDAM have been placed haphazardly in this square. By starting at the bottom left-hand A and moving upwards to the top right-hand M you will find more than one way of collecting all the letters of the word in any order. You must tell us how many there are. You cannot move diagonally or collect more than the nine letters of the word.

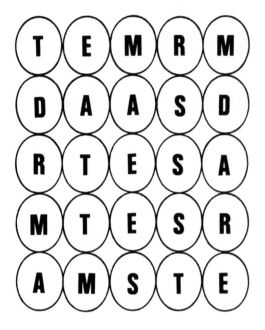

DIAGRAMMATIC In this diagram can you tell us what tiles should replace the missing ones?

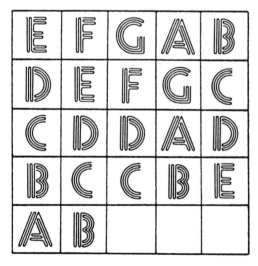

VERBAL   We have arranged the word DEPTH so that it reads the same downwards as across. The intention is to complete the square so that it reads four more words across and down. The first will begin with the E of depth, the second with the P and so on. Can you tell us what word begins with the letter 'H'? Here are all of the letters which you must use to complete the square:

E E E E E E

Y W N N A

R R

```
D E P T H
E
P
T
H
```

MATHS   On a railway track we find a tunnel which is five miles long. A train, 440 yards long, enters the tunnel at a speed of 50 miles per hour. How long will it take for the whole of the train to pass completely through the tunnel?

MISCELLANEOUS   A man set out to drive from one town to another. On the first day he covered one third of the total distance. On the second day he covered one half of the remaining distance and on the third one quarter of what was left. On the fourth day, after covering one half of the remaining distance, he was 98¼ miles away from his destination. How many miles has he covered so far?

TRIVIA

1 What is the second hardest mineral to diamond?

2 Who won the 500 cc motorcycle world championship in 1976?

3 What is another name for the knights of *bushido*?

4 Who wrote the piano work *Pictures at an Exhibition*?

5 What is an Ibex?

WORKINGS

ANSWERS

LOGIC   Look at this diagram which has been divided up into sections. Can you tell us which sections can be considered to be the same although the symbols may appear in a different order?

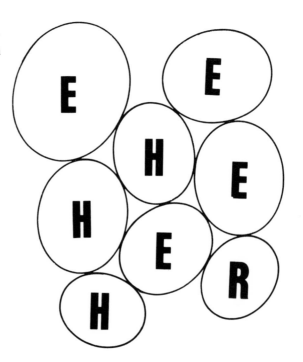

1   2   3   4

A   B   C   D

DIAGRAMMATIC   In the diagram are the letters of the word HERE. Assuming that we can regard each letter as being different, for example the four Es could be E1, E2 etc, how many different arrangements of the letters can you find to form the word?

ERBAL   Can you solve this riddle?

y first is in Mother but not in Son,
y second is in Amble but not in Run,
y third is in Psalm but not in Song,
y fourth is in Flock but never in Throng,
y fifth is in Ears and also in Nose,
y whole is vegetable and grows and grows.

MATHS   During a cricket match Arthur scores 78 more than Bill. Bill, on the other hand, scores 76 runs fewer than Charles. Bill's score and that of Eric total 94 runs. Eric scores 26 runs more than Dennis and Charles scores 26 more than Eric. What is the total number of runs scored by these players?

ISCELLANEOUS   Robin Hood decided at he would give every male in a town of 568 eople nine gold crowns and to every female e offered six gold crowns. Only a certain action of the male population claimed the oney and only half the females collected eir dues. If he gave away a total of 1704 gold owns what fraction of men claimed the oney?

TRIVIA

1 Which British actor of Hungarian descent starred in the 1935 version of *The Scarlet Pimpernel*?

2 What is a Grayling?

3 What is another name for the Australian Sword Lily?

4 Who wrote the book *Elements*?

5 Which member of the Royal family was a gold medallist in the 1972 Olympic Games?

WORKINGS

ANSWERS

LOGIC Look at this series of letters and tell
us what you think they signify.

T T T C W H W

DIAGRAMMATIC Look at the diagram
which can be formed into a cube. Which of the
formed cubes could not be constructed from
the flattened version?

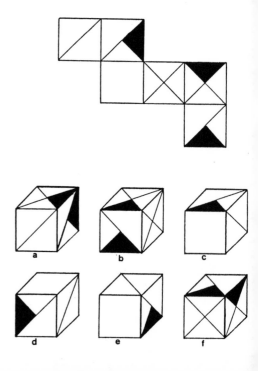

ERBAL You have to place two letters in the brackets so that they finish the word on the left and begin the word on the right. When you read the letters in the brackets downwards you will find a new word. Can you tell us what this word is?

THE ( ) LATE

BOA ( ) RAIN

PAST ( ) ATE

DRESS ( ) CAPE

MATHS How many different ways can you find of scoring 48 by following these rules? You start at the centre and collect a further three numbers from squares that touch by a full side only. All the routes must be different and all must start with the 13. Watch out for reversed routes because these are also accepted.

				10			
		14	11	10			
	14	10	14	11	11		
14	10	14	13	11	14	10	
11	11	14	10	11			
14	10	14					
11							

ISCELLANEOUS Four cars are approaching a crossroads from four different rections. Mr Jones is 22 miles away driving s turbo C5 at 32 mph whilst Mr Smith in his errari is 32 miles away and is travelling at 40 ph. Mrs Brown in her Morris Minor is racing ong at 24 miles per hour and Miss White's ini is maintaining a steady 60 miles per hour. ne Morris is 16 miles from the crossroads hilst the Mini is 47 miles away. In which der will the cars reach the crossroads?

TRIVIA

1 Which American writer wrote *The Last of the Mohicans*?

2 If you suffer from Bright's disease which body organ is affected?

3 Which Queen of Palmyra was defeated by the Roman Emperor Aurelian?

4 In which Dutch town was William the Silent murdered in 1584?

5 Which car engine makes use of a rotating triangle instead of pistons?

WORKINGS

ANSWERS

LOGIC   How many different routes can you find from A to B by following the arrows?

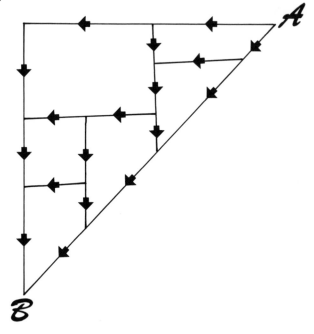

DIAGRAMMATIC   In this diagram you start from any of the four corners, follow the routes and collect any four numbers encountered. You then total these and add the corner number to your total. If you then divide the total by the start number can you tell us how many different ways there are of scoring 8? No more than one corner can be used with each attempt.

VERBAL Can you fill in the two gaps in this sentence with two words of the same six letters?

THE PRICE OF LAMB'S *BLANK* SEEM TO HAVE RISEN IN PROPORTION TO THAT OF *BLANK*

MATHS Can you replace the missing symbols in the following calculation?

(5 ? 13) ? ((9 ? 7) ? 2) = 97

MISCELLANEOUS A cricketer's average in his first 8 innings was 55 runs. After a further 8 innings his average had increased to 90 runs. What was his average for the last 16 innings only?

TRIVIA

1 Who painted *Industry and Idleness*?

2 How many hills can be found in Rome?

3 Which common flower has the Latin name *Calendula officinalis*?

4 Which football league team plays at the Gay Meadow?

5 Who was the woman who flew to Australia in 1930 and established a solo record?

WORKINGS

ANSWERS

LOGIC   In this strange solar system a comet has appeared. It is now 0 degrees in its orbit and will pass planet A when it has covered one quarter of an orbit. Planet A will be at 0 degrees. It will also pass planet A when both it and the comet are three quarters way through their respective orbits. The comet will pass planet B when that planet is at 0 degrees and the comet has covered three eighths of an orbit, and also when the planet and the comet are both five eighths through their orbits. If planet A takes 45 years to orbit the sun, planet B 22 years and the comet 16 years, when will the comet pass each planet?

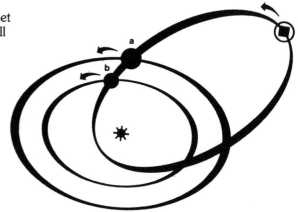

DIAGRAMMATIC   In the diagram you must start at the bottom left-hand corner and work your way up to the top right-hand corner. You can move vertically and horizontally but never diagonally from square to touching square. You cannot collect more than nine numbers at each go. Can you tell us what is the highest score which you can attain?

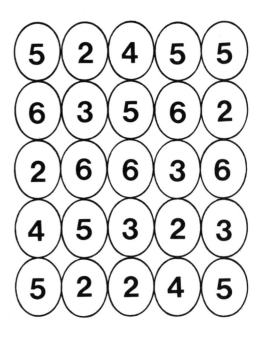

5	2	4	5	5
6	3	5	6	2
2	6	6	3	6
4	5	3	2	3
5	2	2	4	5

VERBAL Replace the first letter of each of ... words either side of the brackets in order to ...ate two new words. Place this letter inside ... brackets and then you will be able to read ...ewly formed word downwards. What is the ...rd?

...AKES ( ) PORT
...EDES ( ) VERY
...AID   ( ) READ
...ALVE ( ) PATCH
...OZE   ( ) CAR
...AIL   ( ) BAKED

MATHS This is a strange dart-board. You throw four darts with each go. Each dart lands and scores. How many different groups of numbers are there which will total 120?

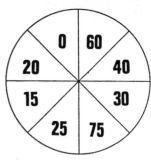

MISCELLANEOUS Over a month five ...ends buy pints of beer as follows: John buys ... more pints than Bill and Bill buys 67 less ...an Charles. Edward buys 19 more pints than ...ennis whilst Charles buys 38 more than ...dward. If Bill and Edward buy a total of 39 ...ts between them, how many pints are ...ught altogether?

TRIVIA

1 In which month is the Autumnal equinox?

2 Which Greek historian died in Thurii in southern Italy?

3 Who wrote the music for the film *Doctor Zhivago*?

4 Who played the lead in the film *Gandhi*?

5 Which British town was called Deva by the Romans?

WORKINGS

ANSWERS

LOGIC In this diagram are the letters of COMB. You must always start at the centre 'C' and move from one square to any other square which is touching it by a full side in any direction except diagonally. Once you have found one set of letters you count that as one and start again. Remember that C B M O can be rearranged to spell COMB and so on. How many different routes can you find?

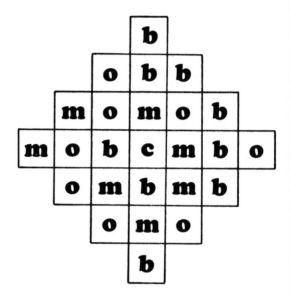

DIAGRAMMATIC In the diagram you must find the segment to start on and then move from segment to segment until you finish on the FINISH segment. You can stop on a segment once but must enter all but one of them. Which segment should you start on? (We have previously given you enough clues for this puzzle!)

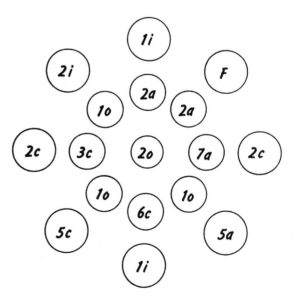

VERBAL By using every letter of this sentence once only, you can find four words closely associated with gases. Can you tell us what they are? Here is the sentence:

NO HEN?', GROANED OUR ONLY FRIEND.

MATHS A ship is trying to get to the safety of an island. It is 15 miles away from it and travels at 10 mph. The rate of flow of the stream against the ship is 2 mph. If the ship uses 5 gallons of fuel every hour and has a tank capacity of 12 gallons can you tell us whether it will reach safety?

MISCELLANEOUS A clock is correct at midnight but gains 22 minutes per hour. You look at the clock and see that it shows 10.15 am. You know that the clock had stopped exactly three hours ago. What is the correct time now?

TRIVIA

1 Which composer wrote *Savitri* in 1908?

2 What is the capital of Panama?

3 Which group of people conquered India in 1526 and ruled it until 1858?

4 Who wrote and composed *Rule Britannia*?

5 Which locomotive was built by George Stephenson in 1815?

WORKINGS

ANSWERS

LOGIC   If Albert has one life and Dennis has four lives but lucky old Fred has six lives how many lives has Thomas?

DIAGRAMMATIC   Look at the diagram and find the squares which can be considered similar because they contain the same number of each of the symbols. Which ones are they?

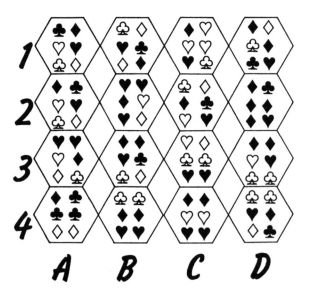

VERBAL   Can you find a three-letter word that fits inside the brackets in such a way that it completes the word on the left and begins the word on the right, thus creating one seven-letter word and one six-letter word?

PLUM (. . .) AGE

MATHS   The following diagram is a strange dartboard. Using three darts at a time you must discover how many different ways there are of scoring a total of 100. Once you have used a combination of numbers you can't use it again in a different order. All darts must score.

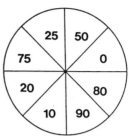

MISCELLANEOUS   A long-distance leaking tanker travels at a speed of 22 mph leaving a trail of petrol behind it which ignited at the moment the tanker set off. The flames follow the tanker at a speed of 20 mph. The tanker stops after 178.75 miles. How long will it be, to the nearest second, before it explodes, that is assuming it does explode?

TRIVIA

1 Which Saint's Day falls on 23 April?

2 Who wrote the novel *Adam Bede* in 1859?

3 Which Greek hero cleaned out the Augean stables?

4 Which Prussian king was also famous as a composer?

5 Are there more than 20 islands in the Hawaii group?

WORKINGS

ANSWERS

17th | Round

LOGIC Each row, column and diagonal line containing five numbers adds up to 120. You must fill in the missing numbers from this group of numbers to discover the value of the question mark. Here are the numbers:

25 18 26 21 24 27 23 30 22

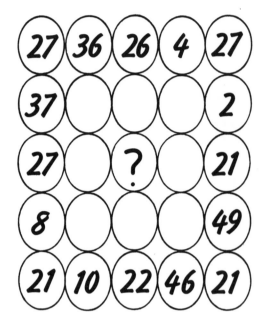

DIAGRAMMATIC In this diagram each of the black circles represent the number −2. Bearing this in mind and starting at the bottom left-hand corner can you tell us how many ways there are of attaining the highest score if you follow the arrows and move to the top right-hand corner? What is the score?

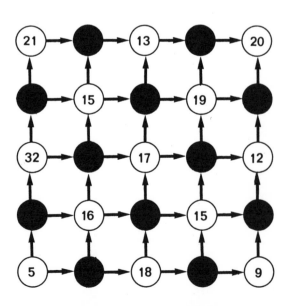

VERBAL Can you change the word FLOCK to the word TRIBE in the least number of moves? You must change one letter at a time and create a good English word at each change. How many moves did you make and what were the words you used?

MATHS Can you work out the logic behind this series and tell us what the numbers represent? Here are the numbers:

7 8 5 5 3 4 4

MISCELLANEOUS Your bath has two taps. The first tap will fill the bath in 15 minutes as long as the plug is in. The other tap would take 7 minutes to accomplish the same function. If the plug is out and the taps are off the bath will empty in 13 minutes. Assuming both taps are on and the plug is out how long will it take to fill the bath to the nearest second?

TRIVIA

1 Which music hall comedian sang 'Keep right on to the end of the road'?

2 Which fashion designer created the A-line?

3 What is the study of birds called?

4 In which country was the early form of man known as Ramapithecus discovered?

5 What disease is a highly infectious one of the skin and is caused by Staphylococci?

WORKINGS

ANSWERS

LOGIC   Each different symbol has a different value. The numbers at the end of each row and column line are the totals of the four symbols in that line. Can you fill in the missing value?

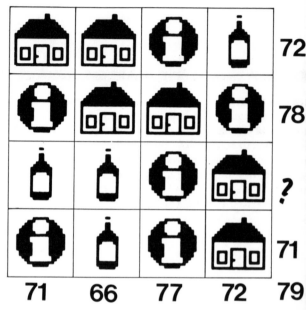

				72
				78
				?
				71
71	66	77	72	79

DIAGRAMMATIC   Another four cars are heading for a crossroads and, guess what, none of them is going to crash. The Mini and the Lada both travel at 20 mph, whilst the Lotus and the 2CV travel at 80 mph. The 2CV has just been fitted with rocket boosters. If the 2CV is 31 miles from the crossroads, the Mini 6 miles, the Lotus 22 miles and the Lada 9 miles in which order will they arrive?

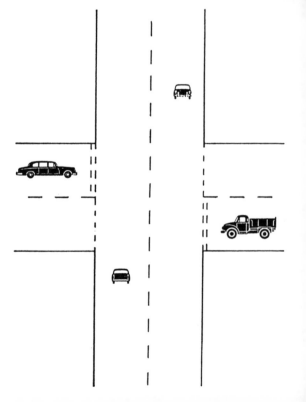

VERBAL   The following groups of letters can be rearranged into words which all have a connection. However, one of the words does not fit in the group exactly. Can you tell which is the most obvious odd one out? You must do a bit of thinking about the words. No more clues!

ONPAR   COMKS   KOFRC   EUDES

MATHS   At a highly exclusive night club the entrance fee is in full pounds only. What would they want with pence? The nightly takings were £7657 and more than 30 people attended. If there were less than one hundred, how many customers were there and how much was the entrance fee?

MISCELLANEOUS   A train travels from one town to another. On the outward journey it averages a speed of 285 mph. It is, after all, going down hill – probably at a 90-degree angle! On the return journey over exactly the same distance its average speed is 76 mph. All this may seem highly improbable, but can you tell us what was the average speed for the full journey?

TRIVIA

1 Under which group on the latest driving licence do invalid carriages appear?

2 What is melilot?

3 Who wrote *The Lion, the Witch and the Wardrobe*?

4 What was David Bowie's real name?

5 Who set the land speed record for a wheel-driven car at Lake Eyre in 1964?

WORKINGS

ANSWERS

LOGIC This archaic departures board in a Middle Eastern airport shows the following: The flight to Delhi is delayed by 858 hours. The flight to Osaka is delayed by 858 hours and the flight to Sydney is delayed by 715 hours. Well, they are having a revolution at the moment. The delays have some relationship to the letters in the names of the cities, however. When you have found out what this is you should have no difficulty in discovering by how many hours the Stockholm flight is delayed.

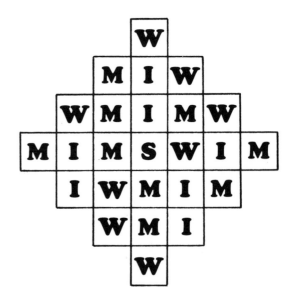

Delhi   858

858 Osaka

Stockholm   ?

715 Sydney

DIAGRAMMATIC In this diagram there are the letters of the word SWIM. You begin at the centre letter, move from square to touching square and collect the four letters of the word in any order. By touching we mean by a full side, not just a corner. If you can collect the same group of four letters in a reversed order that counts as being different. How many different ways are there of accomplishing the task?

VERBAL   Can you replace the blanks in this sentence with two five-lettered words which are composed of the same letters? Here's the sentence:

' WAS DIFFICULT TO KEEP *BLANK* IN CAVE TIMES BECAUSE THEY HAD TO BE CARVED ON *BLANK*.

MATHS   In a town of 3550 people there lived a philanthropist. He offered each male inhabitant £45 and each female £60 as a gift. Of the males only one ninth claimed the money and of the females one twelfth made their claim. After all it was the holidays so he wasn't such a philanthropist after all! Can you tell us how much he gave away altogether?

MISCELLANEOUS   If you look at the diagram you will see that two planets are peacefully in orbit around a star. Both move clockwise. The outer planet takes 14 years to complete an orbit whilst the inner one takes nine years. At the moment the planets are in line with each other and their sun. Can you tell when they will next form a line with each other and their sun?

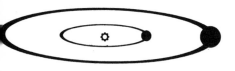

TRIVIA

1 Which businessman who became a millionaire at the age of 22, lived in the UK and founded a museum in Malibu?

2 Where would you find the former British liner *Queen Mary*?

3 Which national flag consists of a green star on a red background?

4 Which king of England suffered periods of madness and later became permanently insane?

5 What was the name of the Egyptian bull god?

WORKINGS

ANSWERS

LOGIC Each different symbol has a different value. The numbers at the end of each row, column and diagonal line are the totals of the four symbols in that line. Can you fill in the missing value?

56
55
56
56

55   58   ?   58   55

DIAGRAMMATIC Look at the diagram and tell us how many squares of any size you can construct in it.

Below are some words written on oth sides of brackets. You must change the st letter of each word with another in such a ay that two different words are now formed. ace the letter within the brackets and then ad the letters downwards. You will find that ey create a courtly word. What is the word?

ALE   ( ) SAME

APE   ( ) RATION

ONIC   ( ) KRIS

ABLE   ( ) FORGE

VARM   ( ) MARRY

AFFIA   ( ) MALES

MATHS You have just returned from the bank. The cashier, however, has made a mistake. He has transposed the pence for pounds. You shouldn't grumble, it gives you quite a bit more cash. Out you go and spend £1.06. You then check your change and to your surprise discover that you now have exactly eight times what you were entitled to receive in the first place. How much ought you to have received from the bank cashier?

ISCELLANEOUS If you look carefully at is set of figures you should be able to puzzle it the relationship between the numbers itside the brackets with the number inside em. Once you have done this you will be le to tell us what should replace the question arks.

54 (85) 653

21 (96) 775

66 (??) 444

TRIVIA

1 Which British cricketer played for Middlesex and England and also played Association football for Arsenal and England?

2 In Greek mythology who was the greatest Greek warrior in the Trojan war?

3 What is the Arabic name for Jerusalem?

4 To whom is the quotation 'Little things affect little minds' attributed?

5 Which Italian composer was ordained as a priest in 1703?

WORKINGS

ANSWERS

LOGIC   Look at this tiled floor from which a section is missing. Work out the logic and tell us what should be used to fill in the gap.

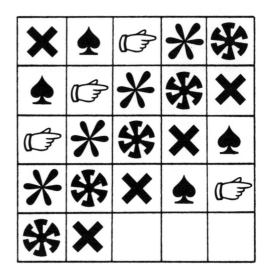

DIAGRAMMATIC   Look at the diagram and by working out the logic fill in the missing value.

Apple	39
Pear	32
Banana	48
Pineapple	?

VERBAL Which five-lettered word can be placed after TOAD, SAND and CLINK in order to form three new words?

MATHS If you look at the following groups of figures you should be able to work out the logic which will enable you to discover the value of the question mark.

$$(20 \quad 4 \quad 11 = 16) \quad (16 \quad 2 \quad 5 = 13)$$
$$(21 \quad 3 \quad 9 = 16) \quad (25 \quad 5 \quad 10 = \quad ?)$$

MISCELLANEOUS You look at the change in your piggy bank. It totals £73.35 and is made up of an equal number of five coins of the realm. You have 45 coins of each value. Can you tell us what the coins are?

TRIVIA

1 Which French philosopher and scientist was imprisoned in the Bastille before going into exile in England?

2 How many islands are there in the Faeroe group?

3 By what other names were the royalists known in the English Civil War?

4 Which Israeli statesman was known as the Father of the Nation?

5 Who was the leader of the Oxford Movement and professor of poetry at Oxford between 1831 and 1841?

WORKINGS

ANSWERS

LOGIC   Look at this diagram of three scales. Can you work out the logic and tell us what ought to replace the question mark?

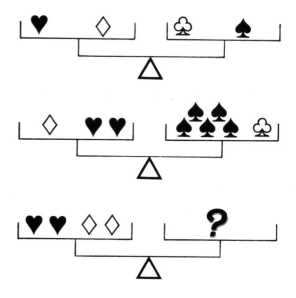

DIAGRAMMATIC   Using this strange diagram you must start at any of the four corners and follow the other lines to four other dots. You add the numbers as you go. You cannot use more than one corner. How many ways are there of scoring exactly 17 by following these instructions?

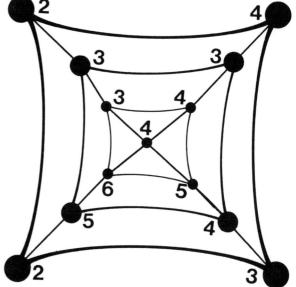

Which four-letter word can you place between the two following words to create two new words, one of nine letters and the other of seven?

PLAIN (. . .) KOK

MATHS Can you replace the question marks with three mathematical symbols so that the equation is completed:

(56 ? 7) ? 9 ? 11 = 6

MISCELLANEOUS Your Mickey Mouse watch was correct at midnight but from that moment began to lose 8 minutes every hour. When you look at the watch, which stopped exactly an hour ago, it shows 4.15 pm. What is the correct time now?

TRIVIA

1 Who was the third President of the USA?

2 What is another name for the wild horse of North America?

3 Which professional boxer was the first to defeat Muhammad Ali?

4 What is another name for the Farne Islands?

5 Who painted *The Burial of Count Orgaz*?

WORKINGS

ANSWERS

LOGIC   In this grid you will notice some of the letters of the word NURSE. You have to fill the other squares with the five letters of NURSE in such a way that no two squares in the same horizontal, vertical or diagonal line are to contain the same letter. A diagonal line can contain any number of squares. Which letter should replace the question mark?

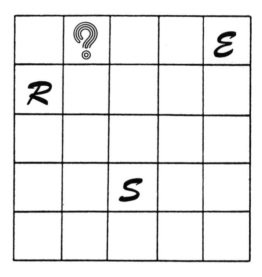

DIAGRAMMATIC   Look at the diagram and find the squares which can be considered similar because they contain the same number of the same symbols. Which ones are they?

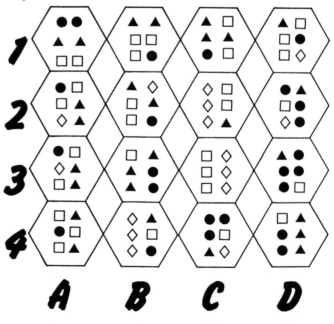

VERBAL By using every letter of this sentence once only, you can find three words closely associated with the solar system. Can you tell us what they are? Here is the sentence:

NOTED REMOTE CAPITALS

MATHS There is a relationship between all the numbers of each triangle. Discover what this is and you should be able to work out the logic which will enable you to discover the value of the question mark

4	6	3	11
56	102	33	?

| 2 | 12 | 14 | 3 | 7 | 4 | 8 | 9 |

MISCELLANEOUS An aeroplane maintains an average speed of 1056 mph from one airport to another. It then returns to the first airport over exactly the same distance at an average speed of 352 mph. What was the average speed for the whole journey?

TRIVIA

1 What is a 'tam-tam'?

2 What was the former name of Constantinople?

3 What is the main constituent of china clay?

4 What name is given to the Japanese art of paper folding?

5 What are all honeybee larvae fed on for a few days at least?

WORKINGS

ANSWERS

LOGIC How many rectangles of any size can you count in this diagram?

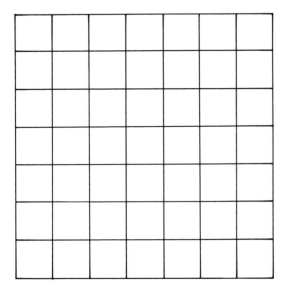

DIAGRAMMATIC Look at the diagram and tell us how many times you can create the word THREE. Treat every E as a different letter along with the others.

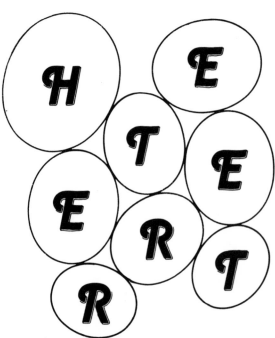

VERBAL   You have to place two letters in the brackets so that they finish the word on the left and begin the word on the right. When you read the letters in the brackets downwards you will find a new word. Can you tell us what this word is?

DOG ( ) STIFF

PAT ( ) AIR

BRA ( ) SET

BAT ( ) ITS

MATHS   You have just returned from the bank. The cashier, however, has made a mistake. He has transposed the pence for pounds. You shouldn't grumble, it gives you quite a bit more cash. Out you go and spend £3.24. You then check the money you have left and to your surprise discover that you now have exactly three times what you were entitled to receive in the first place. How much ought you to have received.

MISCELLANEOUS   Can you work out what should be the next number in the following series of numbers?

3 6 12 24 30 60 ?

TRIVIA

1 Which US actor began his film career by playing gangsters and co-starred with Katherine Hepburn in nine films?

2 Which Spanish artist born in Malaga was also a stage designer?

3 Which German river joins the Rhine at Wesel and has a canal running parallel to it?

4 Where would you find the 'Great Red Spot'?

5 Who wrote the historical novel *I Claudius*?

WORKINGS

ANSWERS

LOGIC Look at this series and tell us which letter you think should come next?

H H E M E J ?

DIAGRAMMATIC Here is another snakes and ladders style of puzzle. You have to get from start to finish. The letters and numbers in each square are highly significant. You start on the bottom line on any of the five squares and have to tell us how many squares away from START this will be. If you land on the bottom of an arrow you follow it to its head.

F	1l	2r	2d	5d	4d
2d	1u	2l	1u	1r	1u
2d	3r	1u	3l	2d	3l
2d	2d	2r		2u	4l
1r	2u	1l	3u	3l	2l
2r	5u	5u	5u	1r	2u
S	4u	3u		2u	4l

ERBAL I am a five-lettered home. Change letter and you could be in trouble. Change a tter of the second word and this time you uld find me on your lapel. Finally change a tter of the third word and go for a sail. What the last word?

MATHS If you look at the diagram you will see that three planets are peacefully in orbit around a star. All move clockwise. The outer planet takes 9 years to complete an orbit, the second takes 7 years, whilst the inner one takes 4 years. At the moment the planets are in line with each other and their sun. Can you tell us when they will next form a line with each other and their sun?

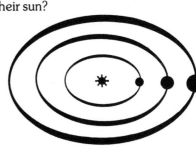

ISCELLANEOUS Your clock is correct at idnight but gains 31 minutes per hour. You ok at the clock and see that it shows 10.45 m. You know that the clock stopped exactly hours ago. What is the correct time now?

TRIVIA

1 Which creatures have a characteristic known as an 'electric organ'?

2 Who composed the Concierto de Aranjuez?

3 What is a parsec?

4 What is another name for a tumblebug?

5 What is the capital city of Ecuador?

WORKINGS

ANSWERS

LOGIC Four little girls are looking for their dogs. Their parents are helping them. They get into their cars and drive round the streets as we can see in the diagram. The squares represent street blocks. Each street block is 4 miles long. Car A passes 11 blocks to get home, car B 13, car C nine and car D eight. If car A travels at 15 mph, car B at 25 mph, car C at 40 mph and car D at 22 mph, which will arrive home first assuming that they all start at the same time?

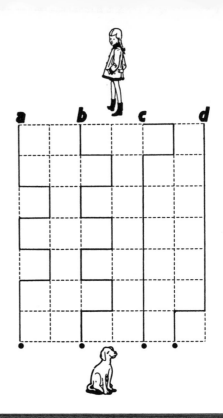

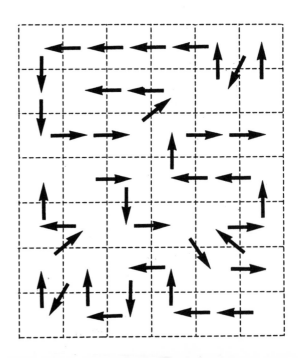

DIAGRAMMATIC Can you find the square which contains the first arrow of the string of arrows which passes through the most squares?

VERBAL Which five-lettered word can be placed before the following words to create four new words? Here are the words:

VINE   SHOT   FRUIT

MATHS A trampess collects cigar ends from which she makes full cigars. She has amassed 435 ends. She knows that she can make one full cigar from 6 ends. How many full cigars can she make and smoke altogether?

MISCELLANEOUS Four cog wheels are in constant mesh. The largest cog has 650 teeth, the next 425 teeth, the next 300 teeth and the smallest has 150 teeth. If they start revolving now, how many revolutions will the largest cog have made before they are back in the same position?

TRIVIA

1 What is the capital of North Rhine-Westphalia, the birthplace of Heinrich Heine?

2 Who was the fifth caliph of the 'Abbasid' dynasty?

3 Who made the first solo non-stop flight across the Atlantic Ocean in 1927?

4 Which obsolete approach to the study of the nervous system believed that the degree of mental development was indicated by the shape of the skull?

5 Which chemical element has the symbol K?

WORKINGS

ANSWERS

LOGIC The diagram is of an unfolded cube. Which of the six cubes below is not a made-up version of the flattened one?

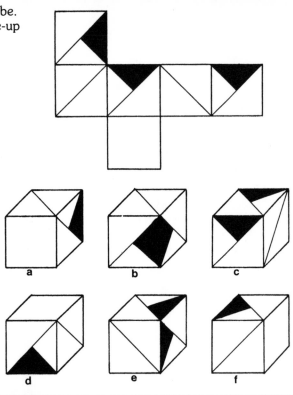

a

b

c

d

e

f

DIAGRAMMATIC You must find the segment in this diagram which will start you off. You will then stop on every segment once only until you finish in the last segment. Here are the clues again: C means clockwise, A means anti-clockwise, I means in and O means out. The numbers signify the number of moves. In which segment should you start?

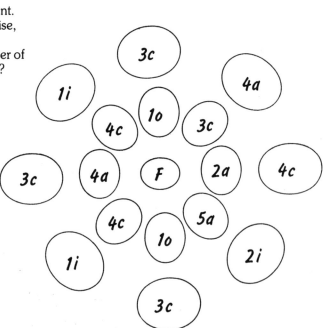

3c

1i

4a

1o

4c

3c

3c

4a

F

2a

4c

4c

5a

1o

1i

2i

3c

VERBAL The groups of letters which follow are jumbled words. You must unscramble the words and find the most obvious odd one out.

PSTAP ALIPU ROLUF RIVEL

MATHS In a game of five players which lasts for exactly 35 minutes, there are two reserves who alternate equally with each player in the team. This means that all the players, including reserves, are on the pitch for the same amount of time. How many minutes for each player is this?

MISCELLANEOUS In a 200-metre race Mary beats Joyce by 20 metres. They decide to run the race again but this time Joyce starts on the 200-metre start-line whilst Mary starts exactly 25 metres behind it. They both complete the race at exactly the same running speed as before. Can you tell us who won the second race?

TRIVIA

1 Which British writer wrote books concerning the life of Jemima Puddle-Duck?

2 What was the philosopher's stone?

3 Which table-tennis player won the singles title at Wimbledon in 1934, '35 and '36?

4 What is the correct name of the 'North Star'?

5 Who composed the overture *Ruslan and Ludmilla*?

WORKINGS

ANSWERS

LOGIC   Here is a map of a one-way street system. Can you tell us how many legal ways there are of getting from A to B?

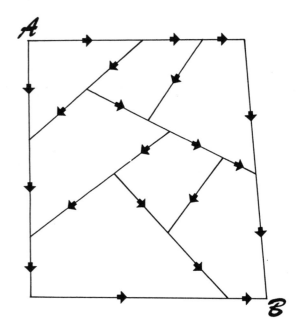

DIAGRAMMATIC   In the diagram the planet orbits the sun once every 13 years. The asteroid has entered an orbit which intersects that of the planet and takes 60 years to complete an orbit. If the asteroid is 60 degrees away from the intersection point when if ever will it collide with the planet?

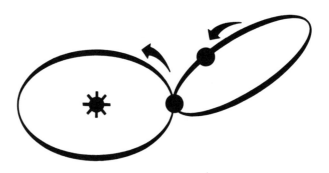

VERBAL   Can you think of a word of three letters which can be added to the end of each of the following words in order to create three other English words? Here are the words:

INES SAND BAR

MATHS   A car travels at a speed of 45 mph. Its fuel consumption is 30 miles to the gallon. It has a 15-gallon tank which was full when it started but at that very moment began to leak fuel. After 250 miles the car stops with a completely empty tank. How many gallons per hour was it losing?

MISCELLANEOUS   Can you read the following message written in code? A code letter represents more than one true letter.

CE EDD EA BDAE DD

DAE DEDEBA

TRIVIA

1 Which dramatist wrote *Les Misérables*?

2 In which county would you find Garstang?

3 What is the other name for the rorqual whale?

4 What is the other name for the flower known as snapdragon?

5 What was the name of the Greek goddess of love?

WORKINGS

ANSWERS

LOGIC   In this grid you will notice that the letters can be used to spell the word SPARK. You have to fill the other squares with the same five letters in such a way that no two squares in the same horizontal, vertical or diagonal line of any number contain the same letter. Complete the square and tell us what should replace the question mark.

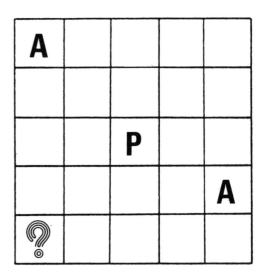

DIAGRAMMATIC   In the diagram you start at any of the four corners and, by following the lines, collect any of the four numbers through which you pass. Add the numbers together along with that of the start corner and then divide the total by the value of the corner. You can only use one corner with each attempt. Can you tell us how many different ways there are of scoring 11 exactly?

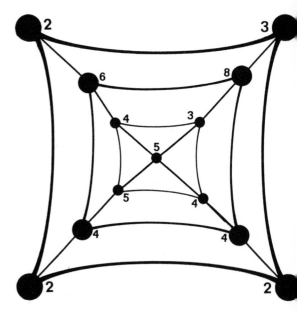

VERBAL HARD can become SOFT by changing one letter at a time. Each alteration, however, must give a new acceptable word. What is the least number of changes you must make and what are they?

MATHS Your motorboat is battling up a stream against a current which flows against it at a speed of 4 mph. It is 20 miles away from safety at the moment and is travelling at 12 mph. It has a tank which contains exactly 6 gallons of fuel at the moment and it uses $2\frac{1}{2}$ gallons every hour. Will it reach safety before the fuel runs out?

MISCELLANEOUS Here is another standard bath. Once again it has two taps and a drainage hole. One of the taps will completely fill the bath in 17 minutes if the plug is in the hole, whilst the other would take 13 minutes to perform the same function. With a filled bath and the taps off the time needed to drain it would be $7\frac{1}{2}$ minutes. Assuming that you have left both taps on and the plug out, how long will it take for the bath to be filled?

TRIVIA

1 Which country owns the Antipodes Islands?

2 Who wrote The Song of Hiawatha?

3 Who continued the work of Thomas Young in deciphering the Rosetta Stone?

4 Who was King of England at the time of the Black Death?

5 How did Lord Kitchener meet his death?

WORKINGS

ANSWERS

LOGIC   Here is a galactic puzzle. The letters of the word CENTAURUS have been placed haphazardly in this square. By starting at the bottom C and moving upwards to the top S you will find more than one way of collecting all the letters of the word in any order. You must tell us how many there are and, by the way, you cannot move diagonally.

A	A	U	R	S
R	U	A	T	U
N	T	A	U	R
E	N	T	A	U
C	E	N	T	A

DIAGRAMMATIC   In this diagram each black circle represents the number −3. You start at the bottom left-hand corner and move upwards to the top right-hand corner by following the arrows. You collect nine numbers in total as you go. If you add these together you will eventually find that there are two totals which can be found once only. Can you tell us what the numbers are?

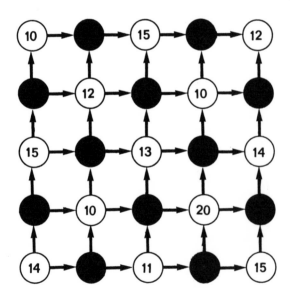

VERBAL We have arranged the word GHOST so that it reads the same downwards as well as across. The intention is to complete the square so that it reads four more words across and down. The first will begin with the H of ghost, the second with the O and so on. Can you tell us what word begins with the letter 'T'? Here are all of the letters which you must use to complete the square:

E E E T T
N I W
C H H R

G H O S T
H
O
S
T

MATHS A rather long train, half a mile to be precise, is about to enter a very long tunnel. The tunnel is 10 miles long. If the speed of the train is 35 mph how long will it take for the whole of the train to pass completely through the tunnel? That is from the very moment the engine enters to the time when the last carriage emerges.

MISCELLANEOUS An aircraft flies from one country to another. On the first day it covers one half of the total distance. On the second day it covers one quarter of the remaining distance and on the third one half of what was left. On the fourth day, after covering one third of the remaining distance, it is 233 miles from its destination. How many miles has it covered so far?

TRIVIA

1 Which pharaoh built the Great Pyramid?

2 In which German town did the Nazi movement begin?

3 In which Dickens novel does Pip appear?

4 Which Greek island was the home of Hippocrates, the physician?

5 What was a kouros?

WORKINGS

ANSWERS

LOGIC   Can you read the following message written in code? To help you the message is a well-known quotation. All the original vowels, however, have been replaced with asterisks. Here is the message:

39★★ 32★3344 22★★3038 3835★★31
3927★ 2137★3927

DIAGRAMMATIC   Each different symbol has a different value. The numbers at the end of each row and column line are the totals of the four symbols in that line. Can you fill in the missing value?

plane	ship	church	gift	206
stadium	church	ship	gift	212
plane	stadium	gift	church	194
ship	gift	stadium	plane	209
204	212	212	193	?

VERBAL   Can you solve this riddle?

My first is in Cheese but not in Milk,
My second is in Cotton but not in Silk,
My third is in Pear and also in Orange,
My fourth is in House but never in Grange,
My fifth is in Perch and also in Nest,
My whole was ridden in the wild, wild west.
What am I?

MATHS   Look at this diagram which has been divided up into sections. Can you tell us which section is the largest in area?

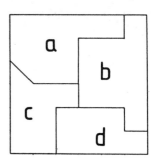

MISCELLANEOUS   Robin Hood has won the Sherwood Forest Pools. He decided that he would give every tenth male in Nottingham 40 gold crowns and every eighth female 64 gold crowns. There were 6,200 people in the town. How much did he give away in total?

TRIVIA

1 Who was the father of Herod the Great?

2 Which is the longest river in the UK?

3 Where might you find 'Chain' and 'Feather' stitch?

4 Who, in opera, was the hero of *The Ring of the Nibelung*?

5 What can be known as 'blue vitriol'.

WORKINGS

ANSWERS

LOGIC   Look at this series of letters and tell us what you think they signify.

T Q S P O

DIAGRAMMATIC   How many squares of any size can you count in this diagram?

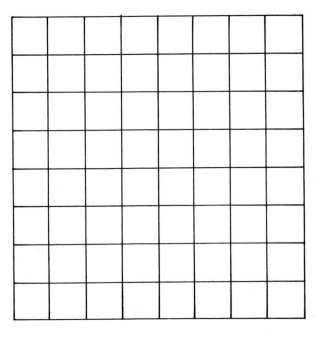

You have to place two letters in the ackets so that they finish the word on the left d begin the word on the right. When you ad the letters in the brackets downwards you ll find a new word. Can you tell us what this ord is?

AT ( ) AT

E ( ) TE

IE ( ) SK

AR ( ) NET

MATHS How many different ways there are of totalling 63 by adding up four numbers. You must always start at the centre 17 and then move from square to touching square. For a square to touch it must do so by a full side. Once the 17 and three other numbers have been collected to total 63 you then count that as one and start again. Reversed routes, on condition that they start at 17, are counted as being different.

			18			
		23	5	18		
	23	5	18	23	5	
18	23	5	17	23	5	18
	23	5	18	5	23	
		5	18	5		
			23			

SCELLANEOUS Here is a quotation with the consonants missing. The vowels have en left in to help you. What is the quotation?

⋆E⋆⋆ ⋆A⋆ ⋆EE⋆⋆ ⋆I⋆ ⋆A⋆E⋆⋆OO
⋆ ⋆A⋆⋆

TRIVIA

1 Which male actor played the lead in the film *Hitler, the Last Ten Days*?

2 If you suffer from agoraphobia of what are you afraid?

3 Which Queen of England engaged in civil war with her nephew, Stephen?

4 Which is the largest city of South Yorkshire in terms of population?

5 Which river flows through Seville?

WORKINGS

ANSWERS

LOGIC   How many different but legal routes can you find of getting from A to B in this diagram? You obviously must follow the direction which is indicated by the arrows.

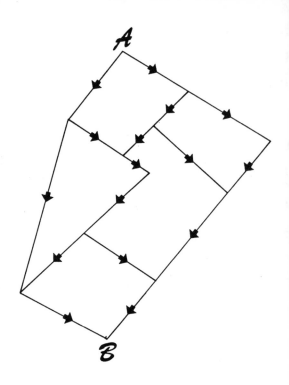

DIAGRAMMATIC   Each of the letters below the diagram should be placed in its correct empty square so that a quotation of sorts emerges. You have to take the letters which we have given you below and place them in the grid provided. The horizontal sequence is correct but the lines have been merged vertically. What is the quotation?

O	D	W	C	R	V	U	B	M
W	H	E	L	A	N	G	O	M
E	M	A	O	R	L	W	N	U
L	B	B	O	U	L	E		T
E		F	E	O		A		T
I		I	H	H		D		
		C						

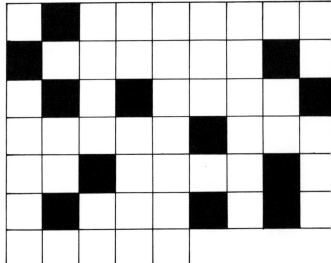

VERBAL   Look at this series of letters and, having discovered the logic behind it, tell us what letter should come next.

L B K C J D ?

MATHS   A fire-engine is travelling to a fire which is 20 miles away. The fire-engine has a tank which contains 15 gallons of water and was full when the vehicle began to move. The engine travels at a speed of 30 mph but its tank has begun to leak 2 gallons each hour. Will it have enough water to put the fire out if 13 gallons will be needed to accomplish the task?

MISCELLANEOUS   You have six matches. How can these be arranged so that they will equal 100?

TRIVIA

1 Which British artist painted *Sarah Siddons as the Tragic Muse*?

2 On whom was the world's first heart transplant operation performed?

3 Which common vegetable belongs to the same family as the tomato?

4 Which football league team is nicknamed the 'Trotters'?

5 Who was the first man to set foot on the Moon?

WORKINGS

ANSWERS

LOGIC   A man cashed a cheque at a bank and discovered that the cashier had transposed the pounds for pence and the pence for pounds thus giving him far more money than he ought to have received. He left the bank and bought goods for £9.52. When he had spent this money he checked his change and discovered that he now had exactly twice the value of the original cheque. What was that value?

DIAGRAMMATIC   The diagram contains the letters of the word EERIE. If we regard each letter as being different, for example the two Rs might be R1 and R2, how many different ways are there of forming the word?

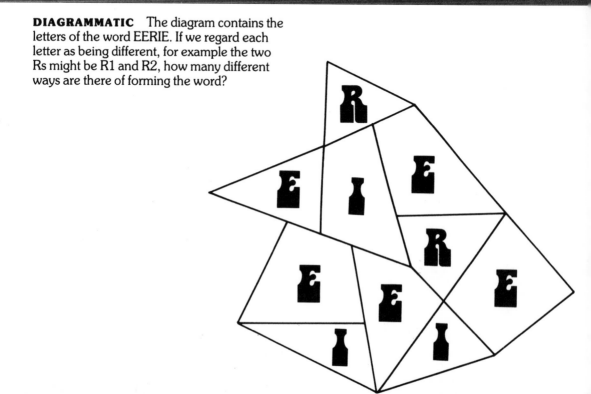

Find the longest word with precious stone connections, which has the second letter H and also contains L and D in that order.

MATHS In this diagram of a strange dartboard there are a certain number of different ways of scoring 135. The rules are that five darts are thrown at a time. Each dart hits the board and scores. How many different ways are there to score 135?

MISCELLANEOUS Your watch was correct at midnight and, at that very moment, began to lose 21 minutes every hour. When you look at the clock it is showing 1 pm and has stopped. In fact it stopped exactly three hours ago. What is the correct time now?

TRIVIA

1 On which day is the winter solstice?

2 Which is the second largest city of Yugoslavia?

3 Who composed the *Scythian Suite*?

4 Who was Minister of Housing and Local Government in 1963?

5 What, in the 18th century at Crockford's, was 'Hazard'?

WORKINGS

ANSWERS

LOGIC   If you get your pencil out you can trace the letters of the word ONYX in any order several times. You must always start at the centre 'O' and move from square to touching square in any direction except diagonally. Once you have found one set of letters you count that as one and start again. Remember that O Y N X can be rearranged to spell ONYX and so on. Reversals are also allowed. How many different routes can you find?

			y			
		x	y	x		
	x	n	y	n	y	
x	n	x	o	x	n	y
	n	x	x	n	y	
		n	x	y		
			x			

DIAGRAMMATIC   Look at the diagram and, once you have found the rationale behind the numbers, work out what should replace the question mark.

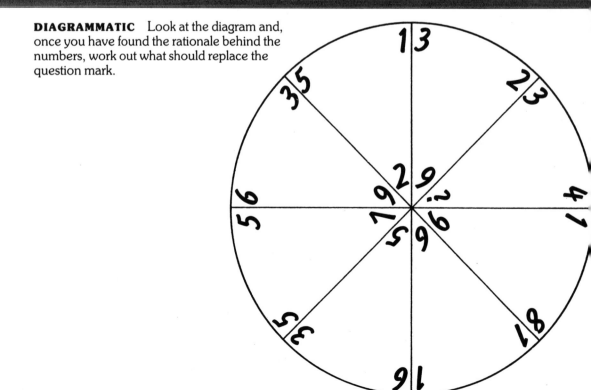

VERBAL Can you complete this word square in such a way that you can read acceptable words both across and downwards? The first word will begin with the B of BEAST, the next with the A and so on. Here are the letters to use:

E E E E E N N N R R S S T T O

B E A S T

MATHS Three planets are in line with each other and the sun. All move in a clockwise direction. The outer planet takes 5 years to complete a full orbit, the next takes 4 years and the innermost planet takes 3 years. Can you work out when they will next form a straight line with each other and the sun?

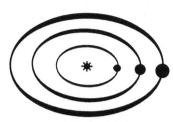

MISCELLANEOUS Look at the following words and, by solving the logic, tell us what the cost of a SATSUMA is? Here are the words:

AVOCADO cost 15p,

CURRANT cost 60p and

RHUBARB cost 36p

TRIVIA

1 What was the title of the film featuring Cliff Richard made in 1961?

2 What is the judicial capital of South Africa?

3 What is Dettifoss?

4 Who composed *Le tombeau de Couperin*?

5 What is the common name given to one of the three Isles du Salut, off the coast of French Guiana?

WORKINGS

ANSWERS

LOGIC In this diagram the squares represent desks. Each desk is 6 feet long. Four secretaries are sauntering to answer the telephone. Secretary A passes nine blocks to get to the phone, secretary B eight, secretary C eleven and secretary D seven. If secretary A saunters at 22 feet per minute, secretary B at 18 feet per minute, secretary C at 16 feet per minute and secretary D at 14 feet per minute, which will arrive at the phone first assuming that they all start at the same time?

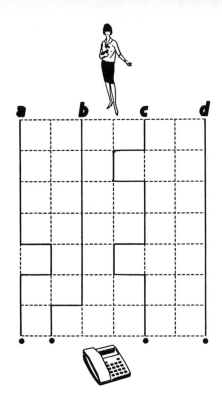

DIAGRAMMATIC Once you have worked out the value of each of the symbols in this diagram you will be able to tell us the total which should replace the question mark. Remember the figures at the end of each column and horizontal line represent the total of the symbols in those lines.

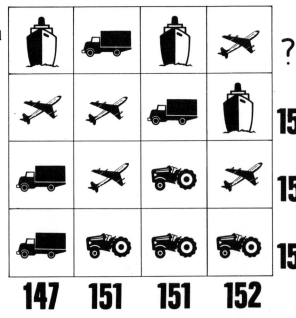

ERBAL Which four-lettered word can be placed before the following words to create three new words? Here are the words:

BALL BARN WAY

MATHS A farmer earned a certain sum by selling eggs. Duck eggs cost four times as much as hen eggs. Of the 555 eggs sold only one fifth were duck eggs. If duck eggs sold at a price of £12.50 for 15 how much money did he earn?

MISCELLANEOUS After stopping at the end of a journey a petrol tanker exploded 2 minutes and 49 seconds later. This is what happened. It started out on a journey and averaged a speed of 65 mph. Unfortunately at the very moment it started on the journey it developed a petrol leak. The petrol caught fire by spontaneous combustion and chased after the tanker. Unlikely, but this is a puzzle. The flames followed the tanker at a speed of 64 mph. How far had the tanker travelled before it stopped?

TRIVIA

1 Who, in Greek legend, killed the Hydra?

2 Which animal is associated with the Egyptian god, Horus?

3 Who, in Hindu mythology, was the god of love?

4 Where would you find Cotopaxi?

5 For what element is Na the chemical symbol?

WORKINGS

ANSWERS

LOGIC   Here is a flattened cut-out of a cube. When it is formed into cubes can you tell us which of the constructed cubes below it cannot be made?

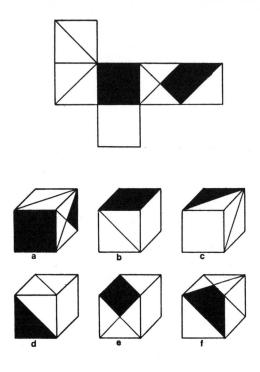

DIAGRAMMATIC   There is logic in this diagram. Discover what this is and then complete the final square.

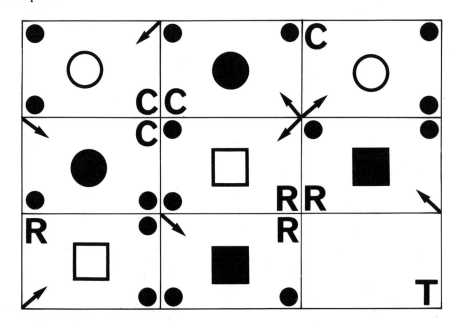

VERBAL Look at the word PREMATURELY. By using some of the letters in the word you should be able to discover three words which will provide answers to the following three clues?

A churchman

Walk over

Foreign currency unit

MATHS In a world speed record attempt a car travels at a speed of 725 mph. Its fuel consumption is 25 miles to the gallon. It has a 16 gallon tank which was full when it started but at that very moment began to leak fuel. After 145 miles the car stops with a completely empty tank. How many gallons per hour was it losing?

MISCELLANEOUS Can you rearrange all these small words so that they will form three larger words with musical connections? There is a ten-letter word, a nine-letter word and an eight-letter word

RIG DO LIST A MOD MAD ERA LINE MAN TO

TRIVIA

1 What is a langur?

2 In which county would you find the Bleasedale Fell?

3 Which bird is also known as the man-of-war bird?

4 Who were the Fates of Norse mythology?

5 Who was the Aztec rain god?

WORKINGS

ANSWERS

LOGIC   In this puzzle every line of five numbers adds up to 175. Can you tell us what should replace the question mark? Here are the missing numbers in a confused order:

29 32 33 33 35 37 37 38 41

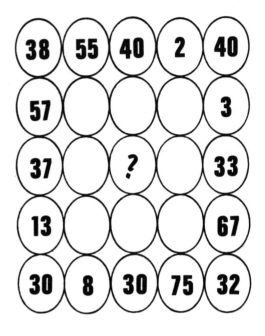

DIAGRAMMATIC   In this diagram you have to find how many different ways there are of totalling 51 by adding up four numbers. You must always start at the centre 13 and then move from square to touching square. For a square to touch it must do so by a full side. Once the 13 and three other numbers have been collected to total 51 you then count that as one and start again. Reversed routes, on condition that they start at 13, are counted as being different.

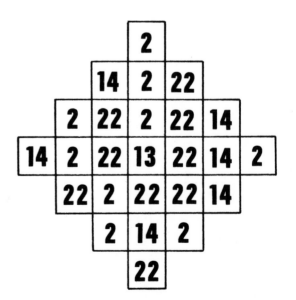

ERBAL Can you solve this riddle?

y first is in Grass but not in Lawn.
y second is in Morning but not in Dawn.
y third is in Odd but never in Strange.
y fourth is in House but nowhere in Grange.
y fifth is in Rose but not in Thorn.
y last is in Died but never in Born.

hat creature am I?

MATHS Scrooge collects cigar ends from which he makes full cigars. He has amassed 689 ends. He knows that he can make one full cigar from 15 ends. How many full cigars can he make and smoke altogether?

ISCELLANEOUS Four cog wheels are in onstant mesh. The largest cog has 68 teeth, e next 42 teeth, the next 30 teeth and the nallest has 24 teeth. If they start revolving ow how many revolutions will the largest cog ave made before all the cogs are back in the me position?

TRIVIA

1 When were the Isthmian Games established in ancient Greece?

2 Where would you find the Liberty Bell?

3 Who wrote *The Cruel Sea*?

4 What is the maximum height of a pony in hands?

5 Which genus of plants includes the sensitive plants?

WORKINGS

ANSWERS

LOGIC   In this grid you will notice that the letters can be used to spell the word SIGHT. You have to fill the other squares with the same five letters in such a way that no two squares in the same horizontal, vertical or diagonal line of any number are to contain the same letter. Complete the square and find the letter which should replace the question mark.

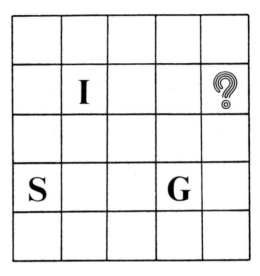

DIAGRAMMATIC   Look at this array of dots and tell us how many squares of any size can be constructed, on the condition that each corner of each square rests on a dot.

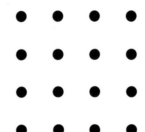

VERBAL TRUE can become REAL by changing one letter at a time. Each alteration, however, must give a new acceptable word. What is the least number of changes you must make and what are they?

MATHS A snail is crawling up to the top of a house. It has to cover the following distances: 140 inches, 135 inches, 55 inches and 25 inches. Its speed over the first distance is 2 feet per hour. Over the second distance it is 2 feet 1 inch per hour and over the third distance it is 2 feet 5 inches per hour. The final distance is covered at a speed of 2½ feet per hour. The snail slides back over the first distance at 3 inches per hour, over the second at 6 inches per hour, over the third at 7 inches per hour and over the last at 8 inches per hour. When will it reach the top?

MISCELLANEOUS Here is a quotation with the vowels missed out. There are also no gaps between the words. Can you tell us what the quotation reads?

**R Y W M N S H L D M R
Y N D N M N**

TRIVIA

1 Over which piece of land was the Seven Years' War fought?

2 Which golfer won three British Open championships, two US amateur championships and four US Open championships between 1959 and 1981?

3 Which pirate's real name was Edward Teach?

4 Who was the wife of Emperor Justinian I?

5 How did St Peter supposedly meet his death?

WORKINGS

ANSWERS

LOGIC   Each different symbol has a different value. The top two sets of scales are in balance at the moment. What should replace the question mark in order to make the third set balance?

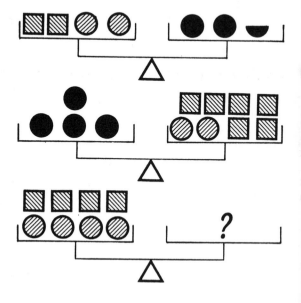

DIAGRAMMATIC   Look at the diagram and tell us what the sentence reads which is coiled within it. You move from square to touching square and, this time, touching by a corner is also acceptable. Find the start square and, as a word of warning, there is one detractor letter which is not used in the sentence. Once again the sentence is a quotation.

Y	R	T	O
I	S	O	S
S	H	I	E
P	H	I	L
O	L	O	P
P	S	A	M
H	Y	O	X
F	R	M	E

VERBAL Below are some words written on both sides of brackets. You must change the last letter of each word with another in such a way that two different words are now formed. Place the letter within the brackets and then read the letters downwards. You will find that they create a very painful word. What is the word?

BAT ( ) SUMMER
ALL ( ) ELK
HAWK ( ) WAITER
DATA ( ) DETAIN
FIR ( ) SKIN
FLEX ( ) CRONY
PECK ( ) MATRON
GLAND ( ) FLUTE

MATHS You have just returned from the bank. The cashier, however, has made a mistake. He has transposed the pence for pounds. You shouldn't grumble, it gives you quite a bit more cash. Out you go and spend £5.32. You then check your change and to your surprise discover that you now have exactly nine times what you were entitled to receive in the first place. How much ought you to have received from the bank cashier?

MISCELLANEOUS Here are five letters. You must convert them into words. The top word has two letters, the next three letters and so on. Each word must increase by one letter and must use the same letters in the same order as the word which precedes it. If the letter was T, for example, the words could read To, Ton, Tone etc. What is your answer?

TRIVIA

1 Who became the first professional English cricket captain in 1953?

2 Which composer wrote *North Country Sketches*?

3 What is the capital of the Dominican Republic?

4 What is a garganey?

5 Of what is a kiloton the equivalent?

WORKINGS

ANSWERS

LOGIC   You are looking at a 20-seater double-decker bus. You can only see one side of it and so you actually see five seats upstairs along with five seats downstairs. You can see that Arthur is seated above Fred and Charles is sitting on the third seat from the front. Eric is sitting at the rear of the bus and on the upper deck. Henry is sitting below Charles. George, on the other hand, is immediately below Bill and one seat ahead of Ian. If John is sitting below Eric where can we find David?

DIAGRAMMATIC   In this diagram we can discover how many of each kind of tree there are in the forest. The number has a relationship to the words. Can you work out what the relationship is and tell us how many birch trees there are?

Birch   ?

Elm   24

Oak   24

Cedar   72

ERBAL Look at the word CHAMELEON
d then, by using some of the letters in the
ord, find the words which answer these three
ues:

Starter fruit with ginger.

Stretch of water.

Sound speed.

MATHS Look at this diagram and tell us
which segments are equal in area.

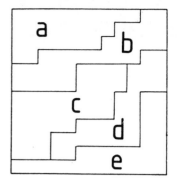

ISCELLANEOUS Look at the diagram and
l us which one is the odd one out.

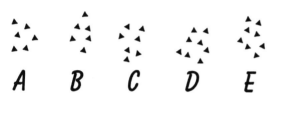

TRIVIA

1 Who launched his solo career with the hit
Maybe I'm Amazed in 1970?

2 Who was the mother of Orpheus?

3 What is a Rhode Island Red?

4 What other name is given to the snout
beetle?

5 Which African carnivorous mammal is also
called the striped weasel?

WORKINGS

ANSWERS

LOGIC   In this puzzle every line of five numbers adds up to 180. Can you tell us what should replace the question mark? Here are the missing numbers in a confused order:

31 33 34 34 36 38 38 39 41

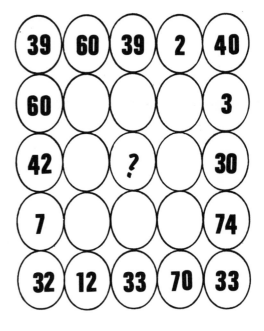

DIAGRAMMATIC   Each of the letters below the diagram should be placed in its correct empty square so that a quotation of sorts emerges. You have to take the letters which we have given you below and place them in the grid provided. The horizontal sequence is correct but the lines have been merged vertically. Can you tell us what the quotation is?

```
O  R  O  O  N  N  R  D  O  H  F  N  R  D  O  U  F
O  U  C  U  O  U  T  R  S  C  A  O  H  A  T  O  U
A  S  K  C  N  T  T  A  Y  K  A  W     Y  O     R
R  C     Y  U  N     Y  W        T        Y     Y
      A  O
```

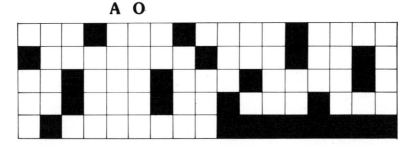

VERBAL Which word of four letters can be placed between these two words so that when is added to the first word it creates another word and when it is added to the front of the second word it creates another word?

...E ( ) GIG

MATHS A sweet manufacturer sells large chocolate eggs at a price of £5 for 10. These eggs, however, are seven times more costly than his small eggs. Of every 189 eggs he sells only one third are large. How much will he make by selling 189 eggs?

MISCELLANEOUS For the same amount of money one can buy 250,000 CHILLIS or 250 OLIVES or quarter of a million AVOCADOS. How many ALMONDS can you buy?

TRIVIA

1 What is the capital of Tibet?

2 Which snake, when attacked, sheds its tail which breaks into several pieces?

3 Who was the father of Louis the Pious?

4 Which ancient city was excavated by Kathleen Kenyon between 1952 and 1958?

5 What is the computer language FORTRAN short for?

WORKINGS

ANSWERS

LOGIC   Here is a meadow puzzle. The letters of the word BUTTERCUP have been placed haphazardly in this square. By starting at the bottom B and moving upwards to the top P you will find more than one way of collecting all the letters of the word in any order. You must tell us how many there are and, by the way, you cannot move diagonally.

C	T	U	T	P
E	T	T	C	C
T	R	T	E	U
U	R	T	T	E
B	U	T	T	R

DIAGRAMMATIC   In this diagram you must work out what the letters represent. Once you have done this it should be easy to discover the two segments which are the odd ones out.

ERBAL Here are three letters: E G A. The E [is] the second letter of a capital city and the G [a]nd A are included in the name of that city in [th]at order. What is the longest capital city you [c]an find to fulfil these conditions?

MATHS A cricketer's average for his first 20 innings was 14½ runs. After a further 25 innings his average had increased. If his overall average now stands at 20.8 runs can you tell us what his average was for the last 25 innings?

[M]ISCELLANEOUS Two words have been [m]erged together here. One word runs from [le]ft to right and the other from right to left. [T]hey have rather hilly connections. Can you [te]ll us what the words are?

[A] U N A A R P F G U R N U

[N] A J

TRIVIA

1 Who wrote *Lycidas* in 1637?

2 What is the common name for the herbaceous plant *Helleborus niger*?

3 Which bird with purple plumage resembles a moorhen and is able to run over floating vegetation?

4 What is the common name for the frog, *Astylosternus robustus*?

5 Which British churchman was nicknamed the 'Gloomy Dean'?

WORKINGS

ANSWERS

LOGIC Look at this dart board. Assuming that you throw five darts at a time and that each of the darts always hits the board and scores, how many different ways are there of scoring 275?

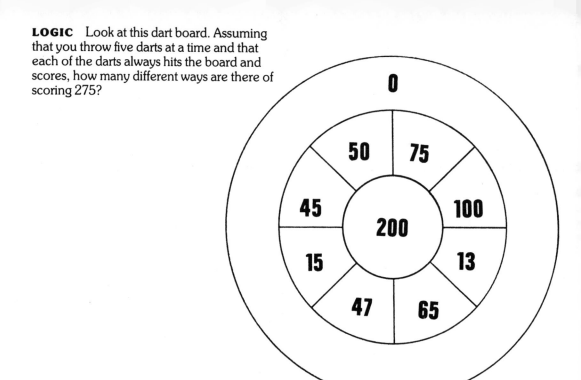

DIAGRAMMATIC In the diagram are the letters of the word TUTU. Assuming that we can regard each letter as being different, for example the four Ts could be T1, T2 etc, how many different arrangements of the letters can you find to form the word?

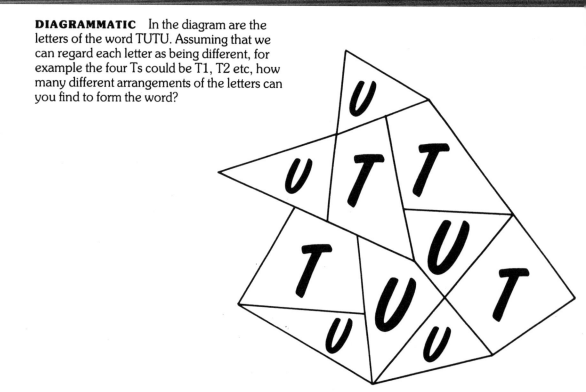

VERBAL You must complete this word square so that it reads acceptable words both downwards and across. The second word will begin with the U of JUDGE, the next with the D and so on. What words will complete the square?

These are the letters which you should use:

A B E E E E L L
T T U U V V

```
J U D G E
U
D
G
E
```

MATHS During a cricket match Arthur scores 175 more than Bill. Bill, on the other hand, scores 150 runs fewer than Charles and Bill's score and that of Eric total 152 runs. Eric scores 31 runs more than Dennis and Charles scores 88 more than Eric. What is the total number of runs scored by these players?

MISCELLANEOUS In a zoo there are 500 dogs, 600 cod and 16 vixen. Decide what the logical reason for this is and then work out how many moose there are.

TRIVIA

1 Who wrote the first ever detective story in English?

2 What is a lumpsucker?

3 Who produced the Merlin aircraft engine?

4 What was the old English name for the trombone?

5 What is faïence?

WORKINGS

ANSWERS

LOGIC In this diagram you start at the bottom left-hand corner and move from square to touching square until you collect nine numbers and finish in the top right-hand corner. You cannot move diagonally. What are the highest and lowest scores attainable?

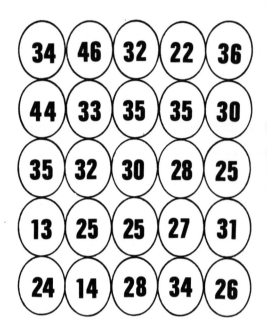

DIAGRAMMATIC Here is a quotation which has been coiled in this diagram. You must find the start letter and tell us what the quotation is. In this instance you can move from square to any touching square even if it only touches by a corner. There are no detractor letters.

T	I	L	M	S	S	P	L	E	T
I	A	E	H	E	W	A	M	A	H
N	A	G	H	A	E	V	R	E	G
I	O	R	T	L	P	E	O	O	I
E	N	U	L	E	L	O	R	L	N
M	T	I	E	N	R	E	L	U	G
I	E	F	S	T	O	U	A	T	O

VERBAL   I am a four-lettered kind of butter. Change one letter and I have a little fun. Change another letter and I must run. Finally change my last letter and I am useful with electricity. What is the last word?

MATHS   A fire-engine is travelling to a fire which is 50 miles away. The fire-engine has a tank which contains 5 gallons of water and was full when the vehicle began to move. The fire-engine travels at a speed of 40 mph but its tank has begun to leak 2 gallons each hour. Will it have enough water to put the fire out if $3\frac{1}{2}$ gallons are needed to accomplish the task?

MISCELLANEOUS   You have five matches. How can these be arranged so that they will equal 25?

TRIVIA

1 What silvery reactive metal was discovered by Sir Humphrey Davy in 1808?

2 What is the largest Eurasian sheep?

3 In the Bible which stronghold was captured by David and, in the New Testament, symbolises Heaven?

4 In which year did the Battle of Ulm take place?

5 What is the capital of Liberia?

WORKINGS

ANSWERS

LOGIC In this diagram the squares represent street blocks. Each street block is 20 miles long. Van A passes ten blocks to deliver its load, van B twelve, van C nine and van D seven. If van A travels at 42 miles per hour, van B at 45 mph, van C 50 mph and van D at 38 mph, which will deliver its load first, assuming that they all start at the same time?

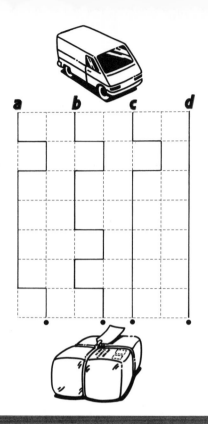

DIAGRAMMATIC Once you have worked out the value of each of the symbols in this diagram you will be able to tell us the total which should replace the question mark. Remember the figures at the end of each column and horizontal line represent the total of the symbols in those lines.

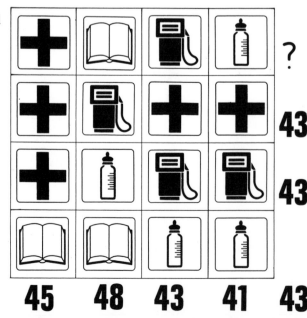

VERBAL Which three-lettered word can be placed before the following words to create three new words? Here are the words:

BAKE   DEW   DAE

MATHS You still have a leaking car. It began to leak the moment you set off and at that time you had 30 gallons of fuel in your tank. If the leak is 11 gallons per hour, your speed 80 miles per hour and your consumption 20 miles per gallon, how many miles will you cover before the tank is dry?

MISCELLANEOUS Three longer words all relating to the home can be formed by adding the correct smaller words together. There are nine small words in total and the three new words are of ten letters each. Here are the small words:

PERM   BED   DOWSE   FEAT

PEP   WIN   ILL   HER   AT

TRIVIA

1 Which European leader was hung upside down in Milan by Partisans?

2 Which German decoration for bravery was instituted in 1813?

3 Which Swedish Island in the Baltic Sea is the largest?

4 Who wrote *Juan in America* in 1951?

5 What is 'bit' short for in computer jargon?

WORKINGS

ANSWERS

LOGIC Here is the plan of a flattened cube. Which of the made up cubes below it cannot be made from the plan?

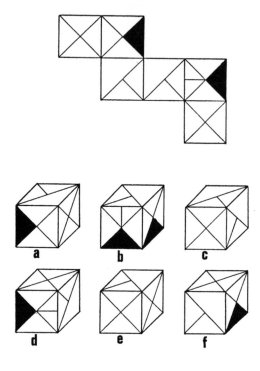

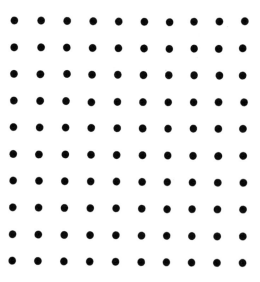

a b c

d e f

DIAGRAMMATIC Look at this array of dots and tell us how many squares of any size can be constructed, on the condition that each corner of each square rests on a dot.

VERBAL   These three letters, I, G and B, are found in the name of a mountain. The I is the second letter and the other two appear in the order given. What is the longest name which can be found?

MATHS   Another snail is crawling up to the top of a house. It has to cover the following distances: 13 inches, 16 inches, 18 inches and 29 inches. Its speed over the first distance is 1 foot 8 inches per hour. Over the second distance it is 2 feet 6 inches per hour and over the third distance it is 3 feet 4 inches per hour. The final distance is covered at a speed of 4 feet 2 inches per hour. The snail slides back over the first distance at 5 inches per hour, over the second at 4 inches per hour, over the third at 6 inches per hour and over the last at 3 inches per hour. When will it reach the top?

MISCELLANEOUS   Which of the following letters can be regarded as the odd one out?

K N F H M

TRIVIA

1 Where was the British Open Championship inaugurated?

2 Which French highwayman was hanged at Tyburn?

3 Which disease of cereals can cause gangrene of the fingers as a result of eating bread made from such cereals?

4 Which precious metal is almost always found in galena ore?

5 What is an icon?

WORKINGS

ANSWERS

LOGIC How many legal ways can you find to get from A to B in this diagram. You can only go the way the arrows point.

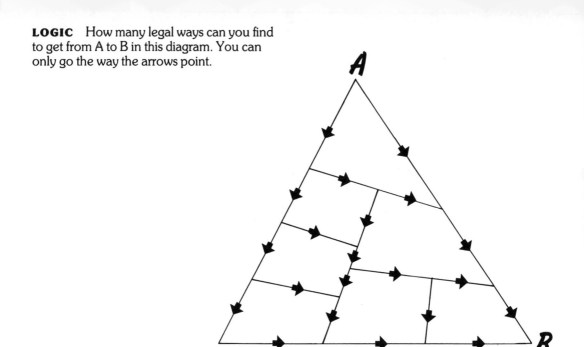

DIAGRAMMATIC Look at this strange dartboard. You use four darts with each try and score 120. Each dart hits the board and scores. How many different ways are there of scoring 120 by abiding by these rules?

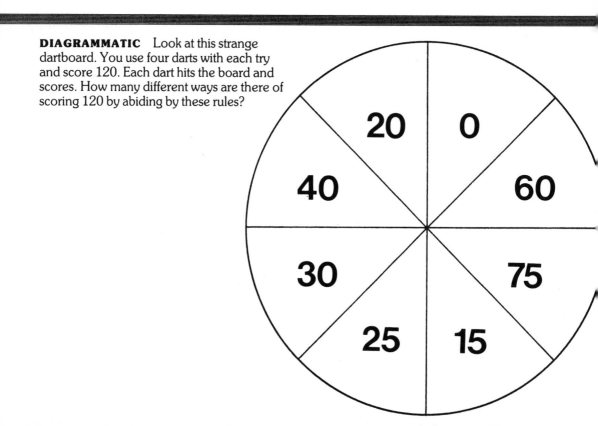

VERBAL   Here is the word ARTICHOKE. By using some of the letters contained in the word you can find the one word answers to these questions:

A great South African journey.

Affluent.

Less liquid.

MATHS   Over 120 days a garage serviced an average of 680 cars. 200 days later the average had increased to 980 cars. What was the average for the last 200 days only?

MISCELLANEOUS   Four cog wheels are in constant mesh. The largest cog has 15 teeth, the next 14 teeth, the next 13 teeth and the smallest has 12 teeth. If they start revolving now how many revolutions will the largest cog have made before all the cogs are back in their original positions?

TRIVIA

1 What is the second highest mountain in Africa?

2 In Greek mythology which gorgon was mortal?

3 With which religions would you associate stupas?

4 When was the 'Popish Plot'?

5 Who was the mother of the emperor Tiberius, who followed Augustus?

WORKINGS

ANSWERS

LOGIC   In this grid you will notice that the letters are some of those used to spell the word CHANGES. You have to fill the other squares with the same seven letters in such a way that no two squares in the same horizontal, vertical or diagonal line of any number are to contain the same letter. What will the completed square look like?

C						
				C		
	S			A		
						N

DIAGRAMMATIC   In the diagram you have to find the maximum number of ways there are of totalling 54. Each way must begin with the 16 and four numbers only are collected. You move from one square to the next which touches by a full side. If there is a way which still begins with the 16 but enters the same three squares as another way albeit in a different order it is classed as another way. How many can you find altogether?

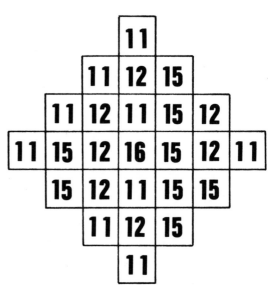

VERBAL   Here is a riddle:

My first is in Apple and also in Pear,
My second is in Head and also in Hair,
My third is in Open although not in Shut,
My fourth is in Knee but never in Foot,
My last is in False and also in True,
My whole is quite often said to be for you.

What am I?

MATHS   Scrooge has returned for a final fling. He has amassed 1042 cigar ends and knows that he can make one full cigar from 17 ends. How many can he make altogether?

MISCELLANEOUS   On a new Beaufort scale cyclones are given a 28 rating, typhoons a 41 rating and tempests an 18 rating. Can you crack the reasoning for this and tell us what the rating is for tornados?

TRIVIA

1 Who wrote the tale of *Rip Van Winkle*?

2 A hermit crab can be found in water and on land. Where else is it occasionally found?

3 Which Portuguese navigator died in India in 1524?

4 What is a jabiru?

5 Who led the Greek resistance to the Italian invasion of Greece in World War II?

WORKINGS

ANSWERS

LOGIC In this puzzle every line of five numbers adds up to 315. Can you tell us what should replace the question mark? Here are some of the missing numbers in a confused order:

60 61 65 65 67

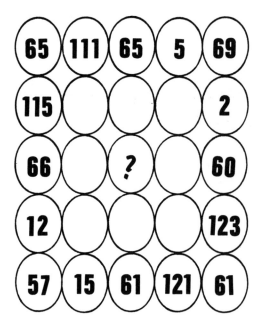

DIAGRAMMATIC Look at the diagram and, by working out the value of each symbol, tell us what value should replace the question mark?

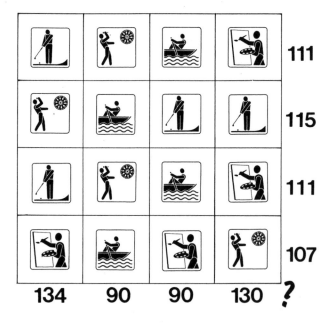

VERBAL Which word of three letters can be placed between these two words so that when it is added to the first word it creates another word and when it is added to the front of the second word it creates another word?

REAL (   ) TILE

MATHS Look at the diagram and tell us which of the segments is the smallest in area.

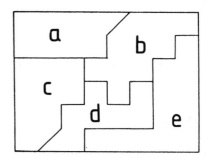

MISCELLANEOUS Two words have been merged together here. One reads from left to right and the other from right to left. What are the words?

B L A A R S D I E L I H C T A A C

1 Which British poet wrote *Poems on Several Occasions* in 1709?

2 In which state of the USA is Yale University?

3 Which French town is the capital of the Eure Department?

4 What is a gaon?

5 What is the Muslim name for the devil beginning with the letter 'I'?

WORKINGS

ANSWERS

1st ROUND ANSWERS

LOGIC   20. The missing figures are placed as follows:

26 25 25
24 20 16
15 15 14

DIAGRAMMATIC   28, each vowel is given the value of 6 and each consonant is given the value of 8.

VERBAL   *LIGHT*.

MATHS   146.

MISCELLANEOUS
There are 2p, 5p, 10p, 20p and 50p coins.

TRIVIA   **1** Aardvark. **2** Coolidge.
3 International Labour Organisation. **4** Louth.
5 Laurence Olivier.

2nd ROUND ANSWERS

LOGIC   2 spades.

DIAGRAMMATIC   There are 3 different scores and they are 55, 49 and 52.

VERBAL   *REST*

MATHS   Times, divide and plus.

MISCELLANEOUS   90 people paying £36.

TRIVIA   **1** Transvaal. **2** Vaughan Williams.
3 Hugh Dowding. **4** Lily-of-the-valley.
5 A computer language.

3rd ROUND ANSWERS

LOGIC   10 times.

DIAGRAMMATIC   9 times.

VERBAL   The words are: *GLASS*, *BRICK* and *STONE*.

MATHS   36.

MISCELLANEOUS   Average speed is 240 miles per hour. No, you can't add the speeds together and divide by two because we are dealing with finite distances.

TRIVIA   **1** Japan. **2** Anne Brontë. **3** St Denis.
4 A freshwater fish. **5** Iridium.

4th ROUND ANSWERS

LOGIC   91. There is a formula for doing this, but we won't tell you what it is!

DIAGRAMMATIC
45. There is a formula for this one as well.

VERBAL   Cheetah.

MATHS   6. Three series of numbers are intermingled.

MISCELLANEOUS   23 insects.

TRIVIA   **1** Bismarck. **2** England.
3 Donnington **4** Joseph of Arimathea. **5** A unit of force.

5th ROUND ANSWERS

LOGIC   J, (keys on a typewriter).

DIAGRAMMATIC
Three squares from the start square marked 3U.

VERBAL   *SIGHT*. The other words are *EIGHT*, *FIGHT* and *LIGHT*.

MATHS
20 years. The planets are on opposite sides of the sun.

MISCELLANEOUS   5 pm.

TRIVIA   **1** Parliamentarians. **2** Hugo. **3** Vulture.
4 Hargreaves. **5** Three.

6th ROUND ANSWERS

LOGIC   Baby A. Baby A takes 2 minutes and 50 seconds. Baby B takes 3 minutes and 47 seconds. Baby C takes 4 minutes and 4 seconds. Baby D takes 4 minutes and 40 seconds.

DIAGRAMMATIC
The start square is the top right-hand corner square.

VERBAL   *ELECT*.

MATHS   78 cigars. Remember after he has made his first batch he can smoke them and have another set of ends left.

MISCELLANEOUS   96 revolutions. If the largest cog has made 96 revolutions, the next cog will make 352 revolutions, the next 396, and the smallest 495. This is the least number of revolutions possible before they are all back at the start position.

TRIVIA   **1** Deucalion. **2** Bobby Jones. **3** Mohs.
4 Toad. **5** Pecos.

LOGIC   B.

DIAGRAMMATIC   You start on the inner circle on segment '1o' at the three o'clock position.

VERBAL   *PROTO* or *TROOP*. The other words read *SABRE*, *SPEAR* and *LANCE*.

MATHS   48 minutes.

MISCELLANEOUS   John wins.

TRIVIA   **1** Antimony. **2** Chang E. **3** Fort Knox. **4** Giant Clam. **5** Beluga.

LOGIC   There are five ways to collect the letters of Amsterdam.

DIAGRAMMATIC   A G F.

VERBAL   The word is *HYENA*. The other words are: *EVERY*, *PEWEE* and *TREEN*.

MATHS   6 minutes and 18 seconds. The train is ¼ of a mile long and the tunnel is 5 miles long. At 50 mph 5¼ miles is covered in 6.3 minutes or 6 minutes and 18 seconds.

MISCELLANEOUS   687.75 miles.

TRIVIA   **1** Corundum. **2** Barry Sheene. **3** Samurai. **4** Mussorgsky. **5** Goat.

LOGIC   10 ways.

DIAGRAMMATIC   After 123 years.

VERBAL   *MASTER* and *STREAM*.

MATHS   4⅘ gallons.

MISCELLANEOUS   I THINK THEREFORE I AM. This is a simple substitution code. We already know that M = I, from which the rest follows.

TRIVIA   **1** Helen. **2** Lallans. **3** Sidney Bechet. **4** James Hogg. **5** Mecca.

LOGIC   2B, 2D, 3C and 4B; also 3D and 4A.

DIAGRAMMATIC   30 times.

VERBAL   *MAPLE*.

MATHS   338 runs. Arthur scores 100, Bill scores 22, Charlie scores 98, Dennis scores 46 and Eric scores 72 runs.

MISCELLANEOUS
One third. This is another formula puzzle.

TRIVIA   **1** Leslie Howard. **2** Fish. **3** Kangaroo Paw. **4** Euclid. **5** Mark Phillips.

LOGIC   G.

U	D	J	G	E
J	G	E	U	D
E	U	D	J	G
D	J	G	E	U
G	E	U	D	J

DIAGRAMMATIC   1C, 3B and 4D.

VERBAL   5: *MANY, MANE, LANE, LASE, LASS, LESS.*

MATHS   There were 59 people each receiving £25.

MISCELLANEOUS   12 minutes and 38 seconds. There is a formula (which we won't give you), but we will tell you that it is to do with fractions.

TRIVIA   **1** An official of the House of Lords. **2** Tony Hancock. **3** Seismology. **4** Chicago. **5** Egyptian Cobra.

LOGIC   The initials of the British Prime Ministers in reverse order from Margaret Thatcher's third term.

DIAGRAMMATIC   B and E cannot be made.

VERBAL   *RESTORES*.

MATHS   10 possible ways.

MISCELLANEOUS
The order is as follows: Morris, C5, Mini and Ferrari.

TRIVIA   **1** Fenimore Cooper. **2** Kidney. **3** Zenobia. **4** Delft. **5** Wankel.

LOGIC   10 routes.

DIAGRAMMATIC
There are four different ways of scoring 8.

VERBAL   *LIVERS* and *SILVER*.

MATHS   Times, Plus, Plus and Times.

MISCELLANEOUS   107.5 runs.

TRIVIA   **1** Hogarth. **2** Seven. **3** Pot Marigold.
4 Shrewsbury. **5** Amy Johnson.

LOGIC   The comet will pass planet A after 180 years and
planet B after 22 years.

DIAGRAMMATIC   The highest score is 47.

VERBAL   *FALCON*.

MATHS   15

MISCELLANEOUS   211 pints are bought in all. John
bought 85 pints, Bill 5 pints, Charles 72 pints, Dennis 15
pints and Edward 34 pints.

TRIVIA   **1** September. **2** Herodotus. **3** Maurice Jarre.
4 Ben Kingsley. **5** Chester.

LOGIC   There are 18 ways of forming the word COMB.

DIAGRAMMATIC   You start at '1o' on the inner circle at
the seven o'clock position.

VERBAL   The gases are: *RADON, HYDROGEN,
FLUORINE* and *NEON*.

MATHS   Yes, with nearly 3 gallons of fuel left.

MISCELLANEOUS   10.30 am. 615 minutes have
elapsed since midnight. The clock gains 22 minutes *every*
hour therefore each hour is 82 minutes long. If we divide
615 by 22 we get 7.5 or 7.30 am. The clock stopped 3
hours ago therefore the exact time is now 10.30 am.

TRIVIA   **1** Holst. **2** Panama City. **3** Moguls.
4 Thomas Arne. **5** The *Blucher*.

LOGIC   20 lives, based on the value of the first letter of
the name in the alphabet.

DIAGRAMMATIC   1A, 2A and 2C; also 1D and 3B.

VERBAL
The word is *MET*, giving *PLUMMET* and *METAGE*.

MATHS   There are six different ways.

MISCELLANEOUS   After 48 minutes and 45 seconds.

TRIVIA   **1** St George. **2** George Eliot. **3** Hercules.
4 Frederick the Great. **5** Yes.

LOGIC   24. The missing figures are arranged as follows:

25 30 26
27 24 21
22 18 23

DIAGRAMMATIC   The highest score is 85 and there are
four ways of attaining it.

VERBAL   Six moves:
*FLOCK . FLICK . CLICK . CRICK . TRICK . TRICE .
TRIBE*.

MATHS
The number of letters in each month from January to July.

MISCELLANEOUS   20 minutes and 35 seconds.

TRIVIA   **1** Sir Harry Lauder.
2 Christian Dior. **3** Ornithology. **4** India.
5 Impetigo.

LOGIC   65.

DIAGRAMMATIC   The cars arrive at the crossroads in
the following order: Lotus, 2CV, Mini and Lada – What an
incredibly easy puzzle!

VERBAL   The words read *APRON, SMOCK, FROCK*
and *SUEDE*. The last is a material and is therefore the odd
one out.

MATHS   There are 31 people at the nightclub and the
entrance *fee* is £247.

MISCELLANEOUS   The average speed of the train was
120 miles per hour.

TRIVIA   **1** J. **2** A herb. **3** C. S. Lewis. **4** David Jones.
5 Donald Campbell.

19th ROUND ANSWERS

LOGIC   2002 hours. Vowels are worth 11, consonants 13 and they are multiplied. The letter Y is not counted as a vowel since, technically, it is a semi-vowel.

DIAGRAMMATIC   There are 13 ways of collecting the letters of SWIM.

VERBAL   The two words are *NOTES* and *STONE*.

MATHS   £17,750. The very bright ones of you will have discovered a flaw in this puzzle but we are not telling you what it is. If you find it let us know by dropping a note to Mensa, Box 99, Wolverhampton, WV2 4AH.

MISCELLANEOUS   In 63 years. The inner planet is at the 9 o'clock position whilst the outer planet is at the 3 o'clock position.

TRIVIA   **1** Jean Paul Getty. **2** Long Beach, California. **3** Morocco. **4** George III. **5** Apis.

20th ROUND ANSWERS

LOGIC   52.

DIAGRAMMATIC   There are 285 squares in total. Find the formula.

VERBAL   *KNIGHT*.

MATHS   £10.88.

MISCELLANEOUS   The answer is 45. Multiply the first two figures and divide them by the third if they are to the left of the brackets. Then replace the right-hand question mark with this figure. Add the first two figures and subtract the third if they are to the right of the brackets and then replace the left-hand question mark with this figure.

TRIVIA   **1** Denis Compton. **2** Achilles. **3** El-Quds. **4** Disraeli. **5** Vivaldi.

21st ROUND ANSWERS

LOGIC   The missing symbols from left to right are a spade, followed by a hand, followed by a six armed star.

DIAGRAMMATIC   71, each vowel is given the value of 9 and each consonant is given the value of 7. The values are then added together.

VERBAL
STONE to give us Toadstone, Sandstone and Clinkstone.

MATHS   15. You divide the first number by the second and add the third.

MISCELLANEOUS
There are 1p, 2p, 10p, 50p and £1 coins.

TRIVIA   **1** Voltaire. **2** 22. **3** Cavaliers. **4** David Ben-Gurion. **5** John Keble.

22nd ROUND ANSWERS

LOGIC   Two clubs and two spades.

DIAGRAMMATIC
There are 12 different ways of scoring 17.

VERBAL   *SONG*.

MATHS   Divide, plus and minus.

MISCELLANEOUS   7.45 pm.

TRIVIA   **1** Thomas Jefferson. **2** Mustang. **3** Joe Frazier. **4** The Staples. **5** El Greco.

23rd ROUND ANSWERS

LOGIC   U.

N	U	R	S	E
R	S	E	N	U
E	N	U	R	S
U	R	S	E	N
S	E	N	U	R

DIAGRAMMATIC
1B and 4A; 2A, 2B and 3A; 2D and 4C; 3B and 4D.

VERBAL
The words are: *PLANET, ASTEROID* and *COMET*.

MATHS   187. Add the two bottom numbers together and multiply by the top number.

MISCELLANEOUS
Average speed is 528 miles per hour.

TRIVIA   **1** A gong. **2** Byzantium. **3** Kaolin. **4** Origami. **5** Royal Jelly.

LOGIC   784 rectangles.

DIAGRAMMATIC   24 times.

VERBAL   *MACHINED*.

MATHS   £8.28.

MISCELLANEOUS   120 – Old pence in the LSD system.

TRIVIA   **1** Spencer Tracy. **2** Picasso. **3** River Lippe.
4 Jupiter. **5** Robert Graves.

LOGIC   C, (Initials of the names of Tudor and Stuart
monarchs to Charles I from Henry VII).

DIAGRAMMATIC
4U in the bottom right-hand corner square.

VERBAL   *BARGE*. The other words are *LODGE*,
BODGE and *BADGE*.

MATHS   126 years. The outer planet will have
completed 14 orbits, the middle planet will have
completed 18 and the inner planet will have completed
31½ orbits. The outer planet is at 3 o'clock, the second
planet is at 3 o'clock, whilst the inner one is at 9 o'clock.

MISCELLANEOUS   8 pm.

TRIVIA   **1** Fish. **2** Rodrigo. **3** 3.26 light years.
4 Scarab beetle. **5** Quito.

LOGIC   Car C. Car A takes 2 hours and 56 minutes. Car
B takes 2 hours 4 minutes and 48 seconds. Car C takes 54
minutes. Car D takes 1 hour 27 minutes and 16 seconds.

DIAGRAMMATIC   The start square is one below the top
right-hand corner square.

VERBAL   *GRAPE*.

MATHS   86 cigars. Remember after she has made
her first batch she can smoke them and have another set of
ends left.

MISCELLANEOUS   102 revolutions.

TRIVIA   **1** Düsseldorf. **2** Harun al-Rashid.
3 Charles Lindbergh. **4** Phrenology. **5** Potassium.

LOGIC   E.

DIAGRAMMATIC
You start on the outer circle on segment 4c.

VERBAL   *RIVEL* or *LIVER*. The other words read
PASTA, *PILAU* and *FLOUR*.

MATHS   25 minutes.

MISCELLANEOUS   Joyce wins.

TRIVIA   **1** Beatrix Potter. **2** A hypothetical substance
believed to turn base metals into gold.
3 Fred Perry. **4** Polaris. **5** Glinka.

LOGIC   11 ways.

DIAGRAMMATIC   After 130 years.

VERBAL   The suffix is *MAN*, giving the words
LINESMAN, *SANDMAN* and *BARMAN*.

MATHS   1⅕ gallons per hour.

MISCELLANEOUS   THE END OF LIFE IS LIFE ITSELF.
A represents A, F, K, P, U and Z. B represents B, G, L, Q
and V. C represents C, H, M, R and W. D represents D, I,
N, S and X. E represents E, J, O, T and Y.

TRIVIA   **1** Victor Hugo. **2** Lancashire.
3 The humpback whale. **4** Antirrhinum. **5** Aphrodite.

LOGIC   K.

A	P	R	K	S
R	K	S	A	P
S	A	P	R	K
P	R	K	S	A
K	S	A	P	R

DIAGRAMMATIC
There are three ways of scoring exactly 11.

VERBAL   It can be achieved in five moves: *HARD* .
HART . *PART* . *PORT* . *SORT* . *SOFT*.

MATHS
The boat would not reach safety before the fuel ran out.

MISCELLANEOUS   6 hours 54 minutes and 23 seconds
to the nearest second.

TRIVIA   **1** New Zealand. **2** Longfellow.
3 Champollion. **4** Edward III. **5** By drowning.

30th ROUND ANSWERS

LOGIC 22 ways

DIAGRAMMATIC
The totals which can be made are 53 and 57.

VERBAL

```
G H O S T
H I T C H
O T T E R
S C E N E
T H R E W
```

The word beginning with T, therefore, is *THREW*.

MATHS 18 minutes.

MISCELLANEOUS 1631 miles.

TRIVIA **1** Khufu or Cheops. **2** Munich.
3 *Great Expectations*. **4** Cos.
5 A standing nude male figure.

31st ROUND ANSWERS

LOGIC Too many cooks spoil the broth.

DIAGRAMMATIC 188. The value of each symbol is as follows: aircraft are worth 45 each, churches are worth 48 each, cakes are worth 50 each, stadiums are worth 51 each and ships are worth 63 each.

VERBAL *HORSE*.

MATHS B.

MISCELLANEOUS 49,600 gold crowns.

TRIVIA **1** Antipater the Idumaean. **2** Severn.
3 Embroidery. **4** Siegfried. **5** Copper Sulphate.

32nd ROUND ANSWERS

LOGIC The initials of the avoirdupois scale. Ton, Quarter, Stone, Pound and Ounce.

DIAGRAMMATIC 204 squares.

VERBAL *HERITAGE*.

MATHS 10.

MISCELLANEOUS
Every man meets his Waterloo at last.

TRIVIA **1** Alec Guinness. **2** Open spaces.
3 Mathilda. **4** Sheffield. **5** Guadalquivir.

33rd ROUND ANSWERS

LOGIC 7 ways.

DIAGRAMMATIC The quotation reads: 'I wouldn't belong to a club which would have me for a member'.

VERBAL *I*. There are two series intermingled: *A B C D* and *L K J I*.

MATHS Yes, there will be enough water to extinguish the blaze.

MISCELLANEOUS
X X X (Roman numerals and multiply). That is 10 times 10.

TRIVIA **1** Sir Joshua Reynolds. **2** Louis Washkansky.
3 Potato. **4** Bolton. **5** Armstrong.

34th ROUND ANSWERS

LOGIC The original cheque was for £42.95.

DIAGRAMMATIC
There are 210 different ways of forming 'EERIE'.

VERBAL The word is *CHALCEDONYX*.

MATHS There are 17 ways of scoring 135.

MISCELLANEOUS 11 pm.

TRIVIA **1** December 21st. **2** Zagreb. **3** Prokofiev.
4 Sir Keith Joseph. **5** A dice game.

35th ROUND ANSWERS

LOGIC There are 15 ways of forming ONYX.

DIAGRAMMATIC 10. The two numbers in the outer corners of a segment are added together to give the innermost value of the segment directly opposite.

VERBAL
The word square reads:

```
B E A S T
E N T E R
A T O N E
S E N S E
T R E E S
```

MATHS The planets will next be in line with each other and the sun after 30 years. The outer and the inner planets are back at the start position whilst the middle planet is exactly 180 degrees away on the other side of the sun.

MISCELLANEOUS SATSUMA is 19p. The position in the alphabet of the first letter is multiplied by that of the last letter. Thus S is the 19th letter and A is the first letter. These two values are multiplied to give 19.

TRIVIA **1** *The Young Ones*. **2** Bloemfontein.
3 An Icelandic waterfall. **4** Ravel. **5** Devil's Island.

36th ROUND ANSWERS

LOGIC   Secretary A. She takes 2 minutes and 27 seconds. Secretary B takes 2 minutes and 40 seconds. Secretary C takes 4 minutes and 8 seconds. Secretary D takes 3 minutes.

DIAGRAMMATIC   The missing figure is 157. The values of the symbols are as follows: Each ship is worth 40; each truck is worth 39; each aircraft is worth 38; each tractor is worth 36.

VERBAL   *HIGH* to give highball, highbarn and highway.

MATHS   The farmer earned £185.

MISCELLANEOUS   The tanker travelled 195 miles.

TRIVIA   **1** Hercules. **2** Falcon. **3** Kama.
4 In Ecuador, in the Andes. **5** Sodium.

37th ROUND ANSWERS

LOGIC   Cube C.

DIAGRAMMATIC   Note: The symbol in the centre can be replaced by any geometrical figure beginning with the letter T, such as a triangle.

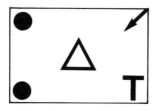

VERBAL
The words are *PRELATE*, *TRAMPLE* and *RUPEE*.

MATHS   51 gallons per hour.

MISCELLANEOUS   The words formed are Mandoline, Madrigalist and Moderato.

TRIVIA   **1** A leaf-eating monkey. **2** Lancashire.
3 Frigate bird. **4** The Norns. **5** Tlaloc.

38th ROUND ANSWERS

LOGIC   The missing number is 35.

DIAGRAMMATIC   There are six ways of making 51.

VERBAL   *GROUSE*.

MATHS   49 cigars. Remember after he has made his first batch he can smoke them and have another set of ends left.

MISCELLANEOUS   210 revolutions.

TRIVIA   **1** 581 BC. **2** Philadelphia.
3 Nicholas Monsarrat. **4** 14½ hands. **5** Mimosa.

39th ROUND ANSWERS

LOGIC   S.

T	S	H	I	G
H	I	G	T	S
G	T	S	H	I
S	H	I	G	T
I	G	T	S	H

DIAGRAMMATIC   20 squares can be constructed.

VERBAL   It can be achieved in 8 moves: *TRUE TREE TRET FRET FEET FEED REED READ REAL*. If you can do it quicker please let us know.

MATHS   It will get there in 17 hours 24 minutes and 30 seconds, to the nearest second.

MISCELLANEOUS   The quotation reads: 'Every woman should marry and no man.'

TRIVIA   **1** Silesia. **2** Jack Nicklaus. **3** Black Beard.
4 Theodora. **5** He was crucified upside down.

40th ROUND ANSWERS

LOGIC 5 black discs. Squares are worth 3, striped circles are worth 7 and black discs are worth 8.

DIAGRAMMATIC The sentence reads 'History is philosophy from examples'.

VERBAL The word reads *MIGRAINE*.

MATHS £7.75.

MISCELLANEOUS The words read:

ME
MET
METE
METER
METERS

TRIVIA **1** Len Hutton. **2** Frederick Delius.
3 Santo Domingo. **4** A dabbling duck.
5 An explosion of 1000 tons of TNT.

41st ROUND ANSWERS

LOGIC David is sitting on the second seat from the front on the upper deck.

DIAGRAMMATIC There are 48 birch trees. Each vowel is worth 3 and each consonant is worth 4. The values of the vowels are added together and this total is then multiplied by the total of the values of the consonants.

VERBAL The words are *MELON*, *LOCH* and *MACH*.

MATHS Segments A and E are of equal area.

MISCELLANEOUS C is the odd one out since it contains an odd number of symbols. The rest are even numbers.

TRIVIA **1** Paul McCartney. **2** Calliope.
3 A domestic fowl. **4** Weevil. **5** Zorilla.

42nd ROUND ANSWERS

LOGIC The missing number is 36.

DIAGRAMMATIC The quotation reads: 'Ask not what your country can do for you, ask what you can do for your country.' The comma is missed out in our puzzle.

VERBAL The word is *FISH* to give pipefish and fishgig.

MATHS The sweet manufacturer made £40.50.

MISCELLANEOUS 25 million. Those letters which are Roman numerals in the word are multiplied thus L times M times D gives 50 × 1000 × 500.

TRIVIA **1** Lhasa. **2** Glass snake. **3** Charlemagne.
4 Jericho. **5** Formula Translation.

43rd ROUND ANSWERS

LOGIC 8 ways.

DIAGRAMMATIC Going clockwise from the 2 o'clock position the segments read CAT (the C and A are in the right-hand segment at the top, whilst the T is in the centre of the opposite segment). Following this process the other segments read ASS, PUP, RAT, APE, COW, PIG and DOG. The odd ones out are COW and PUP since they can relate to several breeds of animal.

VERBAL
The city is *TEGUCIGALPA*, the capital of Honduras.

MATHS
In his last 25 innings the cricketer's average was 25.84 runs.

MISCELLANEOUS
The words are Anapurna and Jungfrau.

TRIVIA **1** John Milton. **2** Christmas Rose.
3 Purple gallinule. **4** Hairy frog. **5** William Inge.

44th ROUND ANSWERS

LOGIC There are 17 ways of scoring 275.

DIAGRAMMATIC 210 times.

VERBAL **J U D G E**
U V U L A
D U V E T
G L E B E
E A T E N

MATHS 643 runs. Arthur scores 220,
Bill scores 45, Charles scores 195, Dennis scores 76 and Eric scores 107 runs.

MISCELLANEOUS There are 1000 moose. All the Roman numerals in the word are added together to give the totals.

TRIVIA **1** Edgar Alan Poe. **2** A fish. **3** Sir Henry Royce.
4 The sackbut. **5** Tin-glazed earthenware.

45th ROUND ANSWERS

LOGIC
The highest attainable total is 286 and the lowest is 233.

DIAGRAMMATIC The quotation reads: 'The lamps are going out all over Europe. We shall not see them lit again in our lifetime'.

VERBAL The last word reads *FLEX*. The words are *GHEE*, *GLEE*, *FLEE* and *FLEX*.

MATHS No, there will not be enough water to extinguish the blaze.

MISCELLANEOUS
L / II (Roman numerals. 50 divided by 2).

TRIVIA **1** Barium. **2** Argali. **3** Zion. **4** 1805.
5 Monrovia.

46th ROUND ANSWERS

LOGIC   Car C. Car A takes 4 hours 45 minutes and 43 seconds. Car B takes 5 hours 20 minutes. Car C takes 3 hours 36 minutes. Car D takes 3 hours 41 minutes and 3 seconds.

DIAGRAMMATIC   The missing figure is 45. Crosses are given the value 10½, baby bottles are given the value 9½, books are given the value 13½ and petrol pumps are given the value 11½.

VERBAL   *SUN* to give sunbake, sundew and sundae.

MATHS   The car covers 160 miles.

MISCELLANEOUS   The long words are Featherbed, Peppermill and Windowseat.

TRIVIA   **1** Mussolini. **2** Iron Cross. **3** Gotland. **4** Eric Linklater. **5** Binary digit.

47th ROUND ANSWERS

LOGIC   Cubes B and E cannot be made.

DIAGRAMMATIC   825 squares can be constructed.

VERBAL   The longest mountain name we can find is Fichtelgebirge in Germany.

MATHS   It will get there in 2 hours 37 minutes and 43 seconds, to the nearest second.

MISCELLANEOUS   The odd letter out is M since it is made up of four straight lines. The other letters are made up of three straight lines each.

TRIVIA   **1** Prestwick. **2** Claude Duval. **3** Ergot. **4** Silver. **5** A religious painting or mosaic.

48th ROUND ANSWERS

LOGIC   There are 10 routes.

DIAGRAMMATIC   There are 15 ways of scoring 120.

VERBAL
The answer words are *TREK*, *RICH* and *THICKER*.

MATHS
The average for the last 200 days was 1160 cars.

MISCELLANEOUS   364 revolutions.

TRIVIA   **1** Mount Kenya. **2** Medusa. **3** Buddhism and Jainism. **4** 1678. **5** Livia.

49th ROUND ANSWERS

LOGIC

C	H	A	N	G	E	S
N	G	E	S	C	H	A
S	C	H	A	N	G	E
A	N	G	E	S	C	H
E	S	C	H	A	N	G
H	A	N	G	E	S	C
G	E	S	C	H	A	N

DIAGRAMMATIC
There are seven ways of scoring exactly 54.

VERBAL   The word reads *PHONE*.

MATHS   Scrooge made 65 cigars.

MISCELLANEOUS   Tornado has a rating of 33. The second and third letters of each word are given their positional value in the alphabet and are then added together.

TRIVIA   **1** Washington Irving. **2** In trees. **3** Vasco da Gama. **4** Stork. **5** Ioannis Metaxas.

50th ROUND ANSWERS

LOGIC   The question mark should be replaced by the number 63.

DIAGRAMMATIC   The question mark should be replaced with a 92. Golfers have been given the value 35, dart players have been given 33, rowers have been given 12 and painters have been given the value 31.

VERBAL   The word is *TOR* to give realtor and tortile.

MATHS   The segment with the smallest area is D.

MISCELLANEOUS
The two merged words are *BASILICA* and *CATHEDRAL*.

TRIVIA   **1** Matthew Prior. **2** Connecticut. **3** Evreux. **4** A Jewish scholar. **5** Iblis.